AN INTRODUCTION TO

NUMERACY TEACHING

13 MAR 1998

by Jessica Brittan

Acknowledgements

We would like to thank the following people for the use of their material:

Shengul Altan, College of North East London, pages 41, 42, 51, 61 and 106, Diana Blofeld, College of North East London, pages 82, 83 and 84, Surrey Adult and Continuing Education Service, pages 56, 80 and 91.

The extracts reproduced on pages 99-102 are reproduced with kind permission of The Open College, which retains all rights to these extracts.

Contents

© The Basic Skills Agency
7th Floor, Commonwealth House, 1-19 New Oxford Street, London WC1A 1NU.

ISBN 1 870741 73 0

Design: Studio 21

First edition published October 1993

Reprinted May 1996

1 | Aspects of Numeracy

This chapter looks at the extent of the numeracy problem in this country and examines the kind of experiences that students may encounter in grappling with numerical concepts. It also looks at the range of ways in which numeracy is taught.

The scale of the numeracy problem

Many of us know people who have problems in dealing with numerical concepts. How often do you hear phrases such as:

"I'm no good at maths"

"Maths was my least favourite subject at school"?

It is, moreover, a problem not confined to any one section of society – many numeracy classes contain students from a wide range of social and occupational backgrounds. Many people, competent in other areas of their lives, face the complexities of our monetary, taxation and mensuration systems without the equipment to deal effectively with them in their everyday or working lives. A casual glance at a newspaper will show the extent to which numerical concepts and language are expected to be understood in, for example, the use of percentages, large numbers, charts and diagrams, temperatures (in the weather report) and in discussion of such topics as the rate of inflation or wage increases. Yet there is a significant proportion of the population to whom these figures appear to be a foreign language.

The provision of numeracy classes has grown in this country alongside that of literacy classes, and in many cases as a direct result of both literacy students and tutors articulating the need for numeracy. As a student tackles his or her difficulties with the language, he or she grows in confidence, and feels up to the challenge that other difficulties present. For students with very basic literacy needs, tackling all but the very simplest paper-based numerical activity is impossible because of the language in which most such activities are couched. Some tutors have developed materials and teaching methods which encourage students to develop language and literacy skills alongside numerical ones. Although this approach is still probably the exception rather than the rule, numeracy tutors have to be aware that their students may also have literacy problems, and that tasks involving reading or writing will have to take account of this. Bilingual students with ESOL needs may not be familiar with either mathematical terminology, or the more practical, contextual approaches to teaching used in this country.

In addition, many colleges of further education have provided numeracy tuition to enable students studying courses, such as business or engineering, to cope with the mathematical content. A recent survey commissioned by ALBSU shows, however, that on average, at least 62% of college students have some problems with numeracy, so it seems that there is a vast need which is as yet not being fully met.

In the population as a whole the need for help with basic skills continues to be considerable. It is currently estimated that almost six million adults in the UK have some difficulty with basic skills including numeracy.

Evidence from the National Child Development Study, which surveyed some of a cohort of 12,500 people born in 1958, when they were 23, and was supplemented by research commissioned by ALBSU in 1986-87, suggested that one in twenty of those adults reported difficulty with numeracy. An ALBSU survey *'Numeracy among Adults'* carried out in 1990 revealed that approximately 12% of adults were unable to carry out a simple addition problem, while greater numbers experienced difficulty with more complex operations.

The definition of basic skills

When we talk about basic skills we mean:

"The ability to read, write and speak English and use mathematics at a level necessary to function and progress at work and in society in general".

In Wales basic skills includes the ability to read and write Welsh for adults whose mother tongue is Welsh.

Our definition of basic skills does not include necessarily wider provision for adults with learning difficulties or other special needs, English as a Foreign Language (EFL) or general access and return to study courses.

The relationship between mathematics and numeracy

Why call it numeracy? Surely what we are talking about is just mathematics given another name? Yes and no – the term numeracy implies that functional element quoted in the definition of basic skills. We are not just talking about the ability to deal with numbers, but to apply them to real-life situations, whether at work or at home. Obviously to work out how much a shopping bill comes to you need to be able to add, and to check your change you need to be able to subtract, but many people who are able to carry out such tasks find it far harder to sit down with pen and paper and work out an addition or subtraction "sum". Conversely, having learned how to perform a mathematical operation in the classroom, people often find it difficult to apply that skill in an everyday situation. Clearly it is not going to be possible or desirable to omit any mathematics whatsoever, but for most students, numeracy teaching will only enable them to deal with real-life situations if it is sensitive to the context in which the numerical problem occurs.

Numeracy tasks commonly undertaken by adults

Most of us have to carry out a considerable number of numerical operations in our daily lives:

- working out shopping bills.

We have to use money to:

- pay for goods both by cash and by cheque
- check our bills, invoices, receipts, wage slips, benefit.

In the shops we are told goods are "10% off!" or "half marked price", and if we want to pay by credit we have to work out how much interest we are paying, and whether we could get a better deal from somewhere else. It may also help us to know whether, if we buy in bulk rather than purchasing smaller items, we are saving money. Also in the shops we may encounter goods sold in pounds, or by the yard, or alternatively in kilograms or by the metre. For anyone brought up to use one system of measurement it is necessary to be able to use the other and to be able to convert between the two.

If we have bank accounts we need to be able to check our statements and to work out the costs of overdrafts and loans. In order to read timetables it is usually necessary to be able to understand the twenty-four hour clock, while more complex but often necessary calculations entail working out the amount of time taken to complete a journey, for example, or whether a two hour video tape is long enough to record a television programme starting at 9.55 and ending at 11.05. How many people would know whether or not they should be worried if the doctor says their temperature is 39 degrees centigrade?

In working life, the demand for manual labour has been shrinking for some time. Many more jobs require some degree of knowledge or skill, and consequently require a greater grasp of basic skills. Numerical skills may be required to handle money, invoices, accounts or budgets, to make precise measurements or estimations, or to interpret charts, graphs or statistical data. Sometimes people lacking in numerical ability use calculators, but how do they know if they have made a mistake if they cannot make an educated guess as to what the correct answer should be?

Students studying in other areas frequently require numerical skills for both academic and vocational subjects. A catering student may need to know how to work out quantities. An engineering student will have difficulty in understanding complex formulae if he or she does not understand fractions. Similarly a business studies student will have difficulty in grasping the rudiments of book-keeping if he or she is not able to use percentages. Tutors already working with numeracy students may well have encountered degree students, in social science, for example, whose progress is hindered by lack of mathematical understanding.

There are many other examples of both numerical skills and of the contexts in which they occur. It is important that numeracy tutors recognise that there are multiple examples in everyday and working life of situations which demand the facility to deal with figures, and that lack of such a facility disables people from handling their own affairs with confidence, and from making informed choices. The job of the numeracy tutor is to give the students the skills and confidence to do this.

How people learn

"A major problem for many tutors is distinguishing between teaching and learning. Unfortunately just because the tutor is teaching it does not mean that the student is learning. Learning can only be accomplished by the student, the tutor's task is to facilitate the process". *An Introduction to Literacy Teaching (ALBSU)*.

Someone who is learning to drive could attend a lecture on driving. He or she could read a book or listen to an experienced friend explain the basic principles. It is very unlikely that anyone would be able to master these principles without getting in the car and attempting to use the controls, however. Equally, it is impossible to find out whether a student has learned something until they actually do it.

For students to learn successfully it is crucial that:

- the skills to be learned are relevant to the student and the student's needs

- the student is actively involved in their own learning process

- the student is allowed to work at their own pace.

It is important to remember that students start at different points, have different goals/ needs and work at different speeds. The best learning programmes are designed to work on strengths and minimise the areas of weakness that the student brings.

Common problems that all teachers experience include:

- how to motivate students

- how to sustain their interest

- how to ensure that they are actually *learning*.

It is very important to be sensitive to the needs of students, even if you are teaching a group of roughly the same ability level. Beware of making general assumptions!

You will encounter numeracy students with little previous mathematical knowledge who will develop skills and confidence quickly. You will find others who, starting from a similar point, struggle for a long time grasping the most basic concepts.

Numeracy has the advantage over literacy in that it is often easier for a student to perceive positive progress. On the other hand it can be more frustrating for a student who is taking a long time to assimilate a concept without which they will find it difficult to progress. One of the most demanding tasks that a numeracy tutor faces is to find a fresh way to explain a problem that has been explained to a student several times without success. Another skill that is equally hard to learn is to allow yourself to stand back, so that the student can grapple with the problem at their own pace, and be allowed to have the opportunity to learn from their mistakes.

Experiences of learning mathematics

Many people express negative feelings about their experiences of learning mathematics at school. Some of these experiences might include:

- being unable to catch up with their class after an absence

- being afraid to ask for help

- being a member of a large class with a teacher too busy to attend to the needs of slower members of the group

- being unable to understand explanations written on the board

- encountering competition from other pupils

- boredom

- inability to concentrate or remember concepts

- disruption in the classroom

- teaching targeted at the more mathematically able members of the group.

It is not uncommon to encounter "maths anxiety" amongst students, who will often express this as a "block" or "barrier" when it comes to learning maths. Often students with negative experiences of learning will focus on mathematics as the subject which provokes the least happy memories of schooling. It may help such students to discuss their experiences with their tutor or in a group – it comes as a relief to students to realise that they are not alone, and that other people have had the same kind of problems.

What may not at first be apparent to the student, but what will become increasingly clear to the numeracy tutor, is that the student may very well be able to perform the mechanics of simple mathematical operations without any real understanding of the underlying concepts. Inability to align addition or subtraction problems, for example, or to multiply a number by ten or a hundred, often indicates lack of understanding of the concept of place value, without which it will be very difficult for the student to make any meaningful progress. Similarly, some students find it very difficult to make the transition to dealing with parts of numbers, after dealing with whole ones.

Consequently the effective numeracy tutor is someone who helps the student to understand the basic concepts, while simultaneously providing the student with a context in which numerical problems occur.

Styles of provision

Numeracy students may have access to more than one style of tuition. In some areas they will be able to choose any learning situation, in others they will have a more restricted choice.

The main choices are:

- group work

- open Learning and drop in

- basic skills support and vocationally and occupationally related teaching

- maths work as part of other support and advice – debt counselling, health advice, supporting parents.

Group work

There are both advantages and disadvantages for students learning in a group. The advantages include:

- cooperation and mutual support amongst members of the group

- realisation that others share similar problems and experiences

- the opportunity to discuss topical subjects and to pool ideas.

The main disadvantage in group work tends to be the difficulty in coping with the range of abilities and knowledge within any one group. Some tutors who have previously taught literacy very successfully in groups sometimes find it hard to come to terms with the fact that it is not always possible to accommodate different ability levels in numeracy groups in quite the same way as it is in a literacy group. Nevertheless, it is possible to design a group session centred around one specific topic if enough material is available to meet a wide variety of needs. Examples of this approach will be discussed in Chapter 5.

Some tutors plan sessions around individual work, encouraging students to work on a variety of skills and topics, according to individual need. They pull the whole class together for a group activity at some time in the session. Others may alternate group and individual sessions. It is important, however, to ensure that in a group situation all individual needs are addressed, both in terms of the skills that students wish to acquire, and of the contexts in which they wish to acquire them.

Open learning and drop-in

Many adult education centres and colleges now contain basic skills open learning centres. There is considerable variance in methods and approaches among the centres, but by and large they are characterised by the following features:

- planned individual tutorials
- easy access to materials and resources
- emphasis on supported independent learning
- access to new technology
- flexible opening times.

In addition, many offer:

- distance learning
- short courses
- discussion groups.

The use of computer assisted learning in open learning centres has become one of their most notable successes, as many students are attracted by the opportunity to use information technology as an integral part of their learning programme.

Open learning has raised the profile of basic skills in many areas, and has certainly affected the development of the basic skills curriculum. It has also been successful in reaching many students who may not have otherwise been attracted by more traditional forms of provision. The more successful schemes offer a wide range of opening times and support students through efficient administrative and record-keeping procedures.

Learning support

The main aim for someone on a vocational course who is experiencing problems with basic skills may simply to be able to cope with the demands of that course. Colleges and training organisations offer several forms of learning support to students on mainstream courses:

- Learning support units, drop-in workshops or open learning centres may provide vocationally related basic skills support.
- Basic skills specialists may be timetabled to work alongside subject specialists, double staffing selected classes. They may also work cooperatively with vocational lecturers in identifying students with basic skills needs and discussing methods, approaches, syllabuses and materials.

- Basic skills support can be integrated into the course programme, either because it is a constituent part of the course, as it is in many Youth and Adult Training Schemes, or as a result of specific needs recognised by vocational tutors and/or senior management.

- In some institutions addressing students' basic skills needs is seen as a staff development issue for all staff. Some colleges are offering vocational lecturers the opportunity to take a City and Guilds qualification in teaching basic skills (9282/3/4), customised to the requirements of students on vocational courses.

Addressing basic skills in other contexts

Not everyone with basic skills needs attends any kind of learning institution, whether basic skills, vocational or academic; in fact, it is only the minority who do. What happens however, if a health authority wishes to run a campaign targeted at the most disadvantaged sections of the local community, but many people in that community have basic skills problems that interfere with the reception of the messages that the authority is attempting to convey? Debt counsellors could face similar problems in dealing with their clients' problems, as could schools attempting to involve parents in developing their children's skills. In cases such as these it may be possible for basic skills specialists to advise and cooperate with the organisations wishing to convey a message, by looking at their publicity and methods of displaying information. For example, a numeracy specialist might advise a health authority intent upon publishing various facts and figures relating to heart disease.

2 | Case Studies

This chapter includes four profiles of students from diverse backgrounds and with different mathematical backgrounds and needs. The case studies will be used in later chapters as a means of illustrating various teaching techniques, styles and approaches. Although it is impossible to illustrate every scenario and student problem you are likely to encounter, these examples should serve to illustrate some of the different approaches and methods you may find useful.

Case Study 1: NADIA

Nadia is twenty-four and has been unemployed since she left school. She is studying part-time on a car mechanics course at a college of further education, which she hopes will lead to employment opportunities.

Nadia is highly motivated, and is trying to improve her numerical skills by attendance at an open learning centre. Like many young people in this country she expresses negative feelings in regard to her experiences of learning mathematics at school:

"I didn't like to ask for help as the teacher was always so busy. When I did get help, I often found there were so many things I didn't understand that it was very hard to grasp the particular thing the teacher was explaining."

Nadia finds the flexibility of the open learning centre helpful in the context of her course. The initial assessment, conducted in the Centre, indicated that the course's mathematical content was causing her considerable difficulty – her numerical ability had not been assessed on entry. Her lecturers had assumed knowledge of formulae and algebraic expressions when in fact she was still struggling was decimals and fractions.

"I feel much more confident that I can complete my course now. I enjoy attending the open learning centre and for the first time in my life I actually enjoy studying maths!"

Case Study 2: ESTHER

Esther is 43, was born in Trinidad and came to this country at the age of 7 where she found it hard to adjust to a different educational system. She is married, with three adult children. **Esther** has had a part-time job as a nursing auxiliary in a hospital for ten years, but finds now that she has more time on her hands, and would like to widen her educational horizons. Rumours of potential redundancies at the hospital have given her an additional impetus to extend her skills and enhance her employability. She enjoys making her own clothes.

In addition to the disruption to her education caused by the move to the UK, **Esther** had an illness at the age of nine which meant that she missed nearly eight months of school. In some subjects she was able to catch up, but not in mathematics.

"Before I became ill I enjoyed maths classes, but afterwards I never really understood what was going on."

Esther is currently attending a 'fresh start' course with the stated aim of progressing to an access course. The course has four hours of numeracy provision, which the tutor devotes to both group sessions, often of topical interest, and to individual learning sessions.

Case Study 3: MATTHEW

Matthew is 51, and lives in a housing estate in Haringey. He is widowed and has a married daughter who lives locally, and a teenage son who lives at home. He has three grandchildren whom he would like to help with their homework. Since losing his wife he likes to get out as much as he can, and is trying to improve his level of educational achievement through attending numeracy and literacy classes. He is interested in cookery, and has thought about operating his own small catering business.

Matthew left school at the age of fourteen without any qualifications. He struggled in classes and became adept at disguising his problems with basic skills. On leaving school he got a job in a factory where he worked until it closed in the early eighties. Since then he has been employed intermittently as a gardener, but is finding this increasingly difficult as he has severe back problems. His weaknesses in basic skills have affected his self-confidence, and it is for this reason, rather than for any chance of improving his employment prospects, that he is attending classes.

The local college provides a range of basic skills classes, enabling **Matthew** to select literacy and numeracy classes appropriate to his needs. He was placed in a group studying for the foundation level of Numberpower.

"I was greatly relieved to find nearly everyone else in the group had the same kind of problems as me! I never feel stupid when I ask for help, like I felt at school!"

Case Study 4: MESFIN

Mesfin is 21 and came to England with his sister as a refugee from Somalia three years ago. He learns quickly, but his education was disrupted by the war. He speaks English reasonably fluently, but has trouble with more specialised and technical vocabulary. He has attended ESOL classes in his borough, and made sufficient progress to feel that he could progress to a vocational course.

Mesfin is currently following a carpentry course, potentially leading to an NVQ Level 2. The NVQ does not itself demand numerical skills, but many of the skills taught in the classroom and the workshop presume knowledge of fractions, metric measurement, areas and perimeters and simple geometry. **Mesfin** has a basic knowlege of maths, but needs help in these areas as well as with mathematical terminology.

There are several students with similar needs in numeracy, whilst at least three of these students have language difficulties. The building department operates a drop-in workshop run by a lecturer who himself has taught on carpentry courses. Many of the students attending are entered for City and Guilds Numeracy examinations, although it is possible that Numberpower may be used in the future. **Mesfin** is currently attending the workshop.

"Sometimes I don't understand the explanations the lecturer is giving. It is really helpful to be able to work at the problem at my own speed".

3 | Assessment, Evaluation and Record Keeping

This chapter looks at some of the methods used to assess students, both when they join provision and in reviewing progress during their course of study. It examines what it is that we are trying to assess, and how the assessment can aid the process of negotiating a learning programme. It emphasises the importance of keeping individual records, and of planning lessons. It also discusses how tutors can evaluate their own teaching.

Assessment

The initial interview and assessment can be the foundation upon which rests students' success or failure. If it is done well, the students will feel more confident about joining a class, and more positive about their prospects. You may find that you are not the person who conducts the initial assessment, rather you will be given information about a particular student on joining the class. Alternatively you may find, as for example, a personal or key tutor in an open learning centre, that you are the one conducting both the initial interview and the assessment. Whatever the case, it is important to understand the assessment process and its implications for learning.

Some schemes will separate the initial interview from assessment, while others will conduct them at the same time. An initial interview will:

- inform students about the different schemes and classes available

- offer advice and guidance

- enable students to identify wider needs and goals

- allow students the opportunity to express anxieties and negative past experiences of learning mathematics.

The environment selected for this purpose should be as private, comfortable and non-threatening as possible. It is important to remember to construct a dialogue with the student, who should be an active partner in identifying and discussing their goals, and in negotiating an appropriate learning programme.

The initial assessment

It is important that all students are assessed at the beginning of a programme so that they can be placed in suitable provision, where a choice of learning and accreditation opportunities are offered, and so that a learning programme can be tailored to their individual needs. Effective assessment will demonstrate to both the tutor and the student:

- the student's strengths and weaknesses

- any underlying problems that may affect learning

- possible problems in understanding key numerical concepts

- a suitable starting point for a learning programme.

Possible underlying problems that may be picked up at this stage if they have not already been identified at the initial interview include:

- difficulties with language, either because the student has literacy needs, or because they are a speaker of other languages. Dyslexic students may invert numbers in the same way they do letters

- any kind of learning difficulty

- visual or auditory difficulties.

There is no one standardised method that tutors use to assess students: some schemes employ a comprehensive assessment package, whereas others rely on a verbal question and answer session. The better models recognise that any kind of situation that reminds students of formal testing procedures is likely to provoke anxiety and inhibit performance.

The initial assessment should reveal both strengths and weaknesses. It should indicate competences that students have already acquired, and should enable them to select others which they wish to achieve. ALBSU has developed a list of competences, published as *The ALBSU Standards for Basic Skills Students and Trainees*, which may assist in this process. A student may, for example, wish to learn how to measure weights and volumes, which can be matched to this competence listed in the *Standards*,

"Measuring Weights and Volumes in Everyday Situations" *(Units 7 and 11)*.

The *Standards* provide the framework for the Certificate in Numeracy Skills (Numberpower), accredited by City and Guilds (see Chapter 4), and can be used to focus student achievement in a form which can be used to gain a qualification.

The case studies provide examples of the use of different assessment procedures.

Matthew

It became evident to the tutor assessing **Matthew** that lack of confidence in his own abilities was a major problem for him. In order to put him at his ease the tutor talked to him about some everyday situations in which he was likely to use numerical skills, for example in working out shopping bills and checking his change. In this way she was able to show **Matthew** that he could in fact carry out some numerical operations. Further discussion elicited the face that **Matthew** felt nervous about the prospects of doing written "sums", stating that he felt he could add and subtract simple numbers ("when you don't have to borrow"), but that was all.

Rather than make **Matthew** do an assessment activity that would reinforce his feelings of inadequacy, the tutor wrote down a couple of simple problems for **Matthew** to solve. As it sounded as if **Matthew** could perform simple addition, the tutor wrote down two or three problems that he would probably be able to complete successfully, and consequently receive a boost to his confidence. Subsequently the tutor gradually increased the difficulty of each problem, until it became apparent that **Matthew** would struggle if assessment progressed. As the tutor thought that **Matthew** might benefit from working towards the foundation level of Numberpower she gave him an activity from ALBSU's *Assessment Pack*.

Nadia

Nadia brought an assignment set by a mechanics lecturer with her to the open learning centre. The assignment involved the use of complex formulae and numbers given to four places of decimals. Discussion between **Nadia** and her tutor revealed that although **Nadia** thought that she had understood decimals and fractions at school, she was not sure how much she remembered. **Nadia** was obviously highly motivated, and accustomed to written assessments on her car mechanics course, so the tutor felt it acceptable to give **Nadia** a more substantial written activity.

The tutor chose this form of assessment, rather than series of written tasks, because she felt it would not resemble a formal test.

At the end of this activity the tutor and **Nadia** discussed the results, and between them developed a learning programme for the immediate future.

Learning plans

Students need a learning plan whether they are part of a group, or learning at their own pace (in an open learning centre, for example). A study programme which takes account of each person's individual abilities, needs, interests and aspirations will help ensure that the student feels adequately supported, motivated and that there is a sense of direction to their studies. In a group situation students will feel that their personal needs are being catered for, while students working in a less structured environment

STUDY PROGRAMME

Name ___Nadia___ Subject ___Maths___

What do you want to work on in the next six weeks	Decimals
	Fractions
	Metric measurement

TOPIC	COMMENTS/SUGGESTIONS
Decimals (Numeracy for core, core book worksheets numbers 234-251)	You seem to understand the basic concept of decimals, so concentrate on addition, subtraction, multiplication and division. You need to look at the use of zeros in decimal numbers, and significant figures
Fractions (Numeracy for core, Core Book worksheets numbers 302-356)	You will need these for algebra Look very carefully at the instructions for handling equivalent fractions before you add and subtract. Take care when dividing by whole numbers
Metric measurement metric/imperial conversion (worksheets 609-660 Assignment No's 12+13)	You must do the practical work first (use practical maths area). You may find the table on worksheet 491 helpful for metric/imperial conversion.

PROGRAMME OF WORK

Name _____ Esther _____ Subject _____ Maths _____

TOPIC			WORKSHEET/RESOURCE/BOOK
Decimals	Book Page No.	📖	'Numeracy for Care' Unit 1
	Worksheet No.	📄	234-251
			Assignment No's 6-9
	Computer Activity	💾	Smile program: Tenners
	Listening Cassette	🎧	'Numeracy for Care' cassette
	Video	📺	A Way with Numbers
		📖	
		📄	
		💾	
		🎧	
		📺	
		📖	
		📄	
		💾	
		🎧	
		📺	

should feel secure in the knowledge that their learning is focused. A learning plan should encourage students to be less dependent on their tutor, as they should know beforehand of areas to be covered, and guidance about resources which may assist them.

An individual action plan should:

- encourage independent learning

- be informed by both initial and on-going assessment

- assist in identifying needs and goals

- be relevant to the learner's expressed needs and goals

- break down learning into achievable "steps"

- be both understandable and coherent

- not be over ambitious, as this may be intimidating and reinforce feelings of inadequacy

- be reviewed on a regular basis.

Matthew and his tutor discussed his needs and aims. The tutor felt that the fact that he could work out shopping bills and check his change was a good starting point, and she suggested a range of activities that would consolidate and extend these skills. She then suggested a little work with addition and subtraction problems, gradually increased in complexity. Subsequently, she suggested further work on applying addition and subtraction to other contexts. As **Matthew** was thinking of working towards the foundation stage of Numberpower, his tutor also suggested assignments which would meet the performance criteria.

Esther's initial discussion and assessment had highlighted the fact that as her long term aim was to be a teacher, and as she needed to either gain at least a "C" grade at GCSE mathematics or pass an entry test set by a teacher training institution, she required an intensive programme that would give a sound grounding in numerical concepts.

Both **Mesfin** and **Nadia** were following vocational college courses, so their action plans concentrated on developing numerical skills in context. In cases such as these the tutor has two jobs:

- to assist the students in identifying their mathematical strengths and weaknesses

- to plan activities which will facilitate and reinforce the acquisition of skills in an appropriate vocational context.

NUMERACY – SELF ASSESSMENT

Name .... Nadia ....

Look at the following problems. Tick the box which applies to you:

	Easy	Hard	I need a little help with
1. If you spend 25p and 46p, how much do you spend altogether?	✓		
2. $406 +$ 279	✓		
3. How much change do you get from £20 if you spend £12?	✓		
4. $78 -$ 23	✓		
5. $204 -$ 197	✓		
6. How much do three 24p stamps cost altogether?	✓		
7. $56 \times$ 5	✓		
8. $34 \times$ 27	✓		
9. If you share £24 among four people, how much does each get?	✓		
10. $208 \div 4 = ?$	✓		
11. $364 \div 14 = ?$	✓		

	Easy	Hard	I need a little help with
11. Write 2 678 043 in words	✓		
12. Convert 3.45 pm to the 24 hour clock	✓		
13. How much is 2046 to the nearest 100?			✓
14. Two pieces of cloth measure 2.4 metres and 0.95 metres. What is their total length?			✓
15. $7 - 0.67$			✓
16. $0.23 \times 0.6 =$		✓	
17. $3.5 \div 0.7 =$		✓	
18. If you earn £200 per week, how much extra do you get if you receive an 8% pay rise?			✓
19. Work out the VAT on a £34 restaurant bill			✓
20. $\frac{3}{4} + \frac{2}{7} =$		✓	
21. $\frac{2}{3} \times \frac{7}{8} =$		✓	

22. Are you familiar with the metric system of measurement (metres, grams, litres, etc)?   Yes/No/A little

STUDENT DETAILS

Name ___Nadia Rachman___ Subject ___Maths___

Tutor ___Jay___ Accreditation (possibly Number power) level 2

Date ___3/2/93___ Date of progress review 17/3/93

Student's long term goals

1/ To successfully complete car mechanics course
2/ To gain employment as a car mechanic

Student learning needs/goals

Nadia needs to revise decimals, fractions, the metric system, percentages, area (especially of circles)
She also needs to be able to interpret long lists of technical and numerical data.
The fractions are important because of the formulae her instructors use. She also needs to learn how to use the memory functions on her calculator to deal with complex calculations

---

Topics/skills to be covered in next six weeks

1/ Revision of decimals

2/ Revision of fractions

3/ Revision of metric system: introduction to metric and imperial conversion.

Planning lessons

A lesson will only be effective if it is thoroughly prepared and planned. It is equally important that the plan for one specific class should relate to an overall scheme of work for the group (if appropriate) and for the individuals comprising it. It may help to concentrate on developing the overall scheme first, as then you may find the individual plan has a clearer focus.

It may help to take into account:

- what exactly you wish the students to achieve
- how this relates to your broader scheme or syllabus
- the disparate needs of individual students
- the pace and type of activity
- methods of ensuring group interaction, whilst allowing people to acquire skills at their own speed
- the resources and materials you may need
- the physical environment you will be working in.

The students in **Esther's** class vary greatly in their ability to handle numbers, yet their tutor is concerned to promote group discussion and mutual support. The crux of the problem for the tutor is how exactly to plan a session involving the whole group while meeting the needs of individuals. In the event, as everyone could at least add and subtract, the tutor decided to look at number of restaurant menus, and ask students to calculate different bills. Students who encountered difficulty with multiplication were given additional supportive material, while more advanced students worked out VAT, service charges and relative value for money of particular restaurants.

Records of work

It is vital that accurate records are kept of students' work: it will also encourage students to be more independent if they keep their own records. It is much easier for both the tutor and the student to check progress if a clear account of the student's work is available, especially in a situation where a student has more than one tutor. This being said, you will find it no easy task to persuade many students to complete records at the end of each session, and you will need to convince them of its importance. Such an opportunity often presents itself during a progress review session, as it is often difficult for a student to recall exactly those activities undertaken in the preceding period if there is no readily available, concise evidence of their achievements. You may also find it of assistance to keep your own records, of both groups and individual activities.

WORK RECORD

Name ...... Matthew Roberts

Title of work	Number	Date begun	Date finished	Comments	Tutor's comments
Introduction to Addition	40 - 50	19/4/93	26/4/93	Just right	You seemed to understand this well.
Money assignments	58 - 70	26/4/93	8/5/93	I need more practice	Try practising some of these skills when you go shopping

Comments you can write:
- Too easy
- Just right
- Too hard
- Interesting
- Boring
- I need more practice
- The instructions were too hard to understand

It should be emphasised that the numbers of pieces of paper that students use as guides should be kept to a minimum – a learning plan and record of work are quite sufficient, and can even be combined if space is allocated on the plan for dates and comments. Obviously the initial interview and assessment will require more paperwork, but on a daily basis there is no reason for overloading a student with unnecessary paper.

Evaluating your teaching

Even experienced numeracy teachers sometimes get it wrong! It is possible to misjudge the degree of competence, motivation or interest in a specific topic held by a group or individuals. Most teachers have had the demoralising experience of carefully preparing a lesson and designing thoughtful and detailed materials which are not appreciated by their recipients! The good news is that this happens less frequently as you yourself develop in skills and confidence. It also helps to evaluate your lessons regularly, so that you can analyse their relative good and bad points.

Questions to ask include:

- Are the stated objectives of the lesson being met?

- Did the lesson appear to involve and interest students of all abilities?

- Were the pace and activities varied enough?

- Was there enough time for all students to complete their tasks satisfactorily?

- Were the materials and resources used easily accessible and understandable?

- Did the organisation of the lesson run smoothly?

- Did students appear to be working competitively, or cooperatively?

- Did you feel that you had a rapport with your students?

- Did you sense that students were enjoying themselves, or did they appear to be frustrated?

The last is the most subjective and arbitrary question to answer, yet you will probably develop a sensitivity to students' emotional responses that will guide you in evaluating your performance, and in consolidating your expertise.

4 | Progress and Accreditation

This chapter looks at how students' progress can be assessed, both in terms of accreditation and less tangible criteria. It stresses the importance of regular progress reviews and discusses the purposes of the types of accreditation available, especially competence-based assessment such as Numberpower. It also looks at the problems and opportunities facing students when they progress.

It can be evident to a tutor that a student has made progress: you may feel that the student has a greater feel for numbers and is finding it easier to apply a skill to a given context, for example. It can often, however, appear less evident to the student. Numeracy has the advantage over literacy in that progress is often quantifiable. There is also a more logical order in which skills are acquired which enables progress to be checked against more specific targets. Students experiencing "maths anxiety" may need more than the evidence of correct answers to feel they have actually made measurable progress, as lack of confidence may affect their evaluation of their own performance (to one person three incorrect answers out of twelve may imply progress, while another will focus on the three incorrect solutions).

It is therefore important to compile a set of objectives or targets with the student against which progress can be measured. It is often helpful to set a regular review period, say, a five or six weekly interval, at which time students have the opportunity to:

- respond to written questions concerning progress or lack of it

- discuss problems with their tutor

- articulate any concerns they may have about the tuition and support they have received

- renegotiate or add to their learning programme

- flag a new interest or change of direction

- review progress in working towards accredited outcomes (e.g. Numberpower).

It may very well be the case that all or some of these items have been dealt with during the normal course of events. The learning review acts as a safety net, to ensure that students do not feel that they have been neglected or their needs or aspirations overlooked.

PROGRESS REVIEW

Name _____ Date _____

What are the main things you have learned or done in the last six weeks?

Did you cover the skills and topics you wanted to?

What did you most enjoy?

What did you feel you did best?

What would you like to practise further?

What would you like to do next?

Students should identify certain targets so that it is easier to assess whether or not those targets have been achieved. **Matthew**, for example, wished to be able to check his bills with confidence, and to have the appropriate skills in addition and subtraction of sums of money. It is important that students understand that incorrect answers are not necessarily symptomatic of a lack of progress. In open learning centres students are encouraged to mark their own work, and to use the correct solution as a stimulus to identifying their own mistakes. This practice has been adopted by many tutors in group situations (please note it is *not* recommended to mark students' work with a series of ticks and crosses accompanied by a mark out of ten or twenty). It can also be difficult to persuade students that even though they have "got the wrong answers", they have made progress because they are using the correct method(s).

The review process may highlight a range of evidence indicating the extent of any progress made:

- students feel their own targets have been met

- analysis of records of work shows a range of tasks and assignments completed at a reasonable time scale

- both students and tutors feel that there is sufficient evidence in a portfolio of work to show that students have achieved a competence outlined in the ALBSU Standards or in Numberpower

- students have performed satisfactorily in self-assessment activities.

It is especially important that a student working in an environment with a flexible mode of attendance, such as an open learning or drop-in centre, is reviewed on a regular basis – this also places some responsibility on the student should there have been any hiccup in the administrative process which regulates and signals that reviews are imminent.

Using accreditation

There is often debate amongst basic skills specialists about the extent to which accreditation of any kind is beneficial to students. An element of ALBSU's quality standards refers to the desirability of making accreditation *available* to all, and that is surely where the emphasis must lie: not every student will need or want a certificate, but should have the opportunity to aim for one should they so desire.

Advantages for students working towards accreditation include:

- increased self-confidence as a result of certifiable achievement

- increased motivation

- familiarisation with accreditation framework, either in respect of working towards an examination or towards competence-based certification

- improvement in study skills

- enhanced opportunities for progression.

An additional factor which may weigh with students educated in other countries is that working towards a certificate in basic skills may very well help them to adapt to practices and procedures commonly adopted by examining and validating bodies in this country.

There are disadvantages, in that some students may find any kind of formal assessment process stressful. This is especially true of exams, but can also be true of competence-based assessment. The constraints of a syllabus or list of competences may deter exploration of other paths, while not all certificates possess "currency" with employers, colleges or training bodies.

Types of accreditation

There are two main routes that students can take to gain certification, namely by passing an examination, or by compiling evidence, usually in a portfolio of completed assignments, that they have reached a specified standard. Various examining bodies offer numeracy, including City and Guilds, the Royal Society of Arts (RSA) and the Associated Examining Board (AEB). Many institutions specialising in basic skills also offer a GCSE in mathematics to adults, providing what may be a more supportive environment in which adults can learn than that provided by a typical college course geared to school leavers.

The most common form of competence-based assessment that you are likely to encounter is Numberpower (City and Guilds), which correlates to the ALBSU Standards. It is offered at three levels: foundation, and stages one and two. It emphasises the kind of numerical competence people are likely to require in their everyday lives, whether at home, at work or while studying on a vocational course at college. This approach can mean that students can accumulate evidence by means other than by completing a worksheet in the classroom. **Mesfin**, for example, measured off pieces of timber in the workshop in order to make a cabinet. This was observed by his vocational tutor, while his numeracy tutor was able to see the finished product.

Numberpower is organised into an accreditation framework such that each stage is divided into units, which in turn are divided into elements. Each unit is presented in a specific format:

- a **description**, which gives a general account of the competence in question

- **performance criteria**, which set out the standards by which activities will be assessed

- the **range**, which indicates the kind of calculations and activities acceptable, examples of contexts, and sources of evidence (such as performance in the workshop)
- **underpinning knowledge and understanding**, which maps the skills that students will need to have in order to acquire the competence.

Description
This unit is concerned with the processes of planning the use of available money and time and keeping basic records.

Element 2·1: Select goods by price
Performance criteria
a) All items are checked that they have the same base unit.
b) The cheapest item is identified.

Range
Types of money: pounds and pence (sterling).
Types of transactions: finding the cheapest of a maximum of five items with different costs but the same base unit, i.e. in terms of volume and capacity (e.g. different brands of soap powder in E4 packets, different brands of beer priced per pint, mineral water priced per litre).
Example contexts
Shopping.
Optional aids: calculator, ready reckoner.
Source of evidence
Performance in the workplace, in personal work projects or through projects/assignments/ simulations over a period of time, supported by personal report and witness testimony.

Underpinning knowledge and understanding
Unit 2·1 – *Select goods by price*
Students/trainees will be expected to know:
- place value of amounts of money
- place value of numbers
- coins and notes and their value
- base units: volume, capacity
- key words/abbreviations: litres – l, centilitres – cl
- how to read amounts of money in figures
- how to put amounts of money in order of value
- how to read base units: volume/capacity
- how to check base units to make sure they are the same

This format is also that used in the framework for National Vocational Qualifications (NVQs). This can help a student's progression from basic skills provision to a vocational course. NVQs break down the skills which underpin an occupation into their constituent parts, and can increasingly be matched to Numberpower and Wordpower competences.

General National Vocational Qualifications (GNVQs) contain a core skills component, which comprises communication skills, numeracy and information technology. The communication skills and numeracy are couched in similar terms to those used by Wordpower and Numberpower, and in many cases are directly comparable.

Progression

Many basic skills tutors assist their students in developing their basic skills to such a level as to increase their prospects of progressing to employment or onto another course. There can however, be a number of hurdles placed in students' way before they can progress:

- Some jobs and courses demand qualifications that students may not have.
- Basic skills qualifications may not constitute "currency" with employers or course tutors.
- There may be negative perceptions of students originating from basic skills provision.
- Students may not wish to progress, if they feel safe and secure in a familiar environment.
- Students may not have study skills adequate to cope with a particular course.
- There can be inadequate support for students who may continue to have basic skills needs even if they do move on.
- Students may move from a fairly safe and secure environment to a more competitive one.
- It may be difficult for adult students to come to terms with being part of a group dominated by younger people.
- There may be entry tests.

Not all of these problems are easily surmountable, but there are some ways in which students' paths can be smoothed:

- Achieving Numberpower and Wordpower can boost a student's confidence, and enable them to move to an NVQ course more easily.
- Whether or not they achieve accreditation, presenting a portfolio of well-organised work can impress interviewers.
- Courses may offer accreditation of prior learning as an alternative to formal qualification.
- Availability of sound educational and careers advice and guidance can assist students considerably.
- Basic skills tutors can assist students in preparing for entry tests.
- Basic skills tutors can assist students applying for specific courses or occupations by ensuring learning programmes and content are focussed on students' long term goals.
- Availability of learning support while studying another subject can considerably affect students' chances of successful outcomes.
- Existence of pre-vocational and course preparation programmes may benefit students.
- Courses specifically geared to adults (e.g. "Access" courses or engineering courses for women returners) can provide more supportive environments for adult learners.

5 | Methods and Approaches

This chapter explores the kinds of topics and skills that could be used with students at different levels, as in the case studies. It also suggests a possible order in which topics could be covered and indicates some of the factors that you may have to take into consideration.

Order of teaching

The basic dilemma for a numeracy tutor relates to the way in which a skill is introduced: should you start with the skill, or with an application? There is no simple answer to this question that will be appropriate to every situation, nor is it necessarily desirable that all tutors should use the same methods. It is important, however, that students are not developing skills divorced from the contexts in which they are likely to encounter them in everyday life. This can be an issue for tutors working with students in an open learning or drop-in environment, where it is sometimes hard to wean students from the practice of completing endless pages of "sums" (or "number-crunching"). This is where the individual learning plan assumes significance, and where it is important to address individual needs and concerns, while at the same time providing a range of quality resources and materials which stimulate interest.

It is often the case that a student will present a problem or interest from which you can extract the mathematical content. You may find, however, that dealing with the skill in question is problematic, in that it presupposes mathematical knowledge which the student may not possess. For example a student on a catering course studying nutrition may be given data relating to nutritional composition of foods in percentages: a problem if the student does not understand the concept of parts of whole numbers.

A group session is very often better structured around a practical application, with supplementary exercises and materials suitable for a range of abilities. What may not be evident however, is that in many cases it is not desirable to select a topic on a arbitrary basis: mathematic skills are usually taught in a specific order, as one concept builds upon knowledge of another.

You will often encounter students who can perform mechanical functions without any real understanding of the underlying numerical concept. This can lead to problems when you ask the student to perform more complex calculations or when discussing which particular skill is applicable to specific context. The most common problem of this nature that you will discover is that a lack of understanding of place value. This may be demonstrated through a student:

- misaligning an addition or subtraction problem

- being unable to estimate or "round off" numbers

- forgetting to "carry" numbers to another column or placing the carried number in the wrong column

- forgetting to add a zero during the second line of long multiplication.

This will become more of a problem for students when they try grouping parts of numbers into tenths, hundredths, etc. without an understanding of place value to whole numbers.

When children are taught place value at school, teachers often employ various physical resources, such as counters, to illustrate grouping of numbers into multiples of ten. This is a little harder with adults, as such activities will be perceived as "childish", and may deter rather than encourage. It soon became clear to **Maureen's** tutor that she had very little understanding of place value, so she decided to use some of the introductory exercises in 'The Numeracy Pack' by Diana Coben and Sandy Black (see page 36). She also discussed money with her, using coins as examples of numbers grouped into multiples of ten. This helped, as **Maureen** was familiar with the idea of 'value' assigned to different notes and coins. The tutor did have to tread carefully at this stage however, as it is possible to appear to be condescending if the subject is not treated sensitively enough.

Esther's tutor was faced with a similar problem, but with a generally more advanced group, she needed to ensure that all students understood the concept before progressing to more complex tasks. She decided first of all to introduce students to the history of numbers and mathematics, demonstrating that origins of mathematics are not grounded in the Western European cultural tradition, and also provoking discussion of different systems of grouping numbers, and the reasons for using groups based on multiples of ten. She then made use of an approach which enabled students to focus on both decimal and whole numbers, by placing a series of numbers in appropriate columns.

Introduction, or reinforcement of the concept of place value, should be followed by skills taught in the following order:

1. Addition (especially of money).	7. Fractions.
2. Subtraction (especially of money).	8. Conversion between fractions and decimals.
3. Multiplication (both simple and long).	
4. Division (both simple and long).	9. Percentages.
5. Estimation and "rounding-off" numbers.	10. Areas, volumes, perimeters.
6. Decimals (some tutors may introduce fractions first).	11. Ratios.
	12. Averages.

Place Value

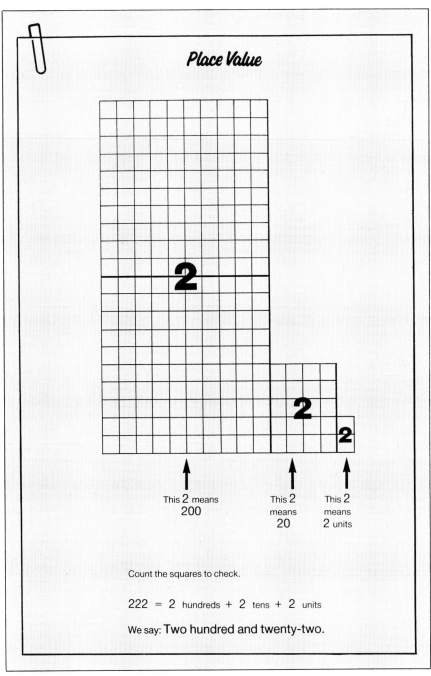

This 2 means
200

This 2
means
20

This 2
means
2 units

Count the squares to check.

222 = 2 hundreds + 2 tens + 2 units

We say: Two hundred and twenty-two.

36

The **twenty-four hour clock** can be introduced at any time once students can add and subtract, although questions involving addition and subtraction of hours and minutes are often demanding. **Metric and imperial measurement** can be introduced when students have a fair understanding of decimals, and in the case of imperial measurement, fractions of quantities, although very simple measurement can be introduced at an earlier stage, especially if students are not likely to progress to working with decimals.

You may find it beneficial to introduce simple **bar charts** at an early stage, as these will provide illustrative material for a number of topics, and they are relatively simple to interpret. **Line graphs, pictograms and pie charts** may have to wait until students understand how to use parts of numbers and how to use scales. **Maps** can be introduced at any stage, although any activity necessitating an understanding of scale and direction is probably better left till a later stage.

It should be emphasised that it is very important, both when giving an oral explanation, and when developing written materials, to break the concepts down into small enough "steps". You may find students are floundering unless you ensure that there are no gaps in your explanation. Obviously the more advanced students are, the fewer the stages you will need to break skills into, but even the more numerically competent student will suffer from inadequate explanations and examples.

Addition

Matthew's tutor started with the premise that he would be more comfortable relating to situations she could already deal with. As there were several other people in the group at a similar level the tutor decided to structure her initial lessons around a discussion of an activity from the foundation level of Numberpower. She encouraged students to discuss how they worked out shopping bills, several of whom stated that they **counted on** from the first number. For example, a student adding 6p to 18p, counted six units forwards from eighteen to arrive at the answer.

What all students who struggle with written addition 'sums' have in common, is the inability to form mental **number bonds** when performing a calculation. People who calculate efficiently do not have to spend time working out "nine plus four", for example, as the answer is already part of that person's conceptual repertoire. Clearly it is important for students without the facility to make use of such number bonds to develop one by taking the opportunity to practice their skills as much as possible. Again it is advisable that the student tackles as many problems of this nature as possible, while a range of different applications is explored.

After the group had explored methods of addition, and the tutor had given students the opportunity to practise their skills, she encouraged them to look at a range of situations where they might have to use addition, and to explore the use of different words and terms to signal when addition should be used (note: this may also be an issue for students with language needs, even if they add perfectly).

Terms which indicate addition:

- **plus**
- **add**
- **added to**
- **........ and ....**

- **total of**
- **sum of**
- **increase by.**

In subsequent lessons the tutor went on to more complex addition problems, ensuring that she covered the following stages thoroughly and gradually:

- addition of single numbers with total of under 10
- addition of single numbers totalling over 10
- addition of double numbers with total of over 10 (no carrying)
- addition of double numbers with total of over 10 (carrying to one column)
- addition of double numbers with total of over 10 (carrying to other columns)
- addition with noughts, e.g. $301 + 60$
- addition of more than two numbers.

Matthew progressed through the first three stages without difficulty, but at this stage some of his answers were incorrect.

Matthew was able to handle money in some everyday situations, as were most of the other students in his class. Most students found that coping with financial paperwork was much more burdensome, however. Understanding the use of money is a vital prerequisite to successful functioning in our society, and the tutor spent most of the time during her initial encounters with **Matthew's** class ensuring that all students were familiar with the basics of our monetary system, including:

- making payments with coins, notes and cheques
- working out costs of shopping bills
- checking change
- budgeting
- checking bills and invoices.

Planning a weekly budget

PERSONAL FINANCES

Skills you need <u>before</u> you begin:

- Understanding of pounds and pence.
- + − money amounts up to £150.00.

Jane works as a clerical assistant and lives at home with her parents.

Her **weekly budget** looks like this:

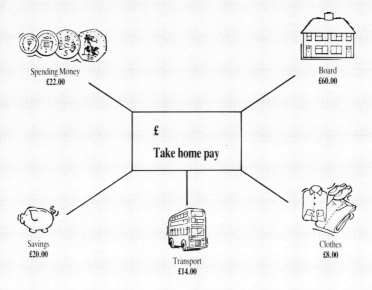

Spending Money
£22.00

Board
£60.00

£
Take home pay

Savings
£20.00

Transport
£14.00

Clothes
£8.00

Add Jane's financial commitments together to find out her weekly take home pay.

You may use a calculator.

Jane has just had a pay rise of £15.00 per week.

Make up Jane's new weekly budget in the same format as above.

You can use this for Numberpower Foundation Unit 2 Element 2

from The Assignment Pack, ALBSU

- planning expenditure
- converting between pounds and pence
- writing amounts of money correctly
- comparing prices.

To this list **Esther's** tutor also added the following:

- using decimalised currency
- calculating shared payments
- working out which purchase gives the best value (is a bulk purchase necessarily better value?)
- selecting investment and credit arrangments.

Using a calculator

You will probably often hear students express the opinion that using a calculator is "cheating". A calculator can be an invaluable tool, however, enabling students to check their work as they progress, alleviating the chore of working out long calculations, and allowing them to concentrate on developing new skills, rather than spending lengthy periods on repetitive tasks. **Matthew** did not know how to use a calculator, and had to be shown. Obviously one of the greatest drawbacks for the numerically inexperienced user is that it is not easy to discover if you have made a mistake: that requires estimation skills which may not be developed until a later stage. **Matthew's** tutor suggested that he always repeat any calculation, and that wherever possible he compared answers with another student.

Esther's tutor demonstrated the use of the memory functions in enabling the user to handle more complex calculations. She also explained the fact that calculators will always omit final noughts after a decimal point, which may cause the unwary to make mistakes when dealing with money. Both students were given assignments which exercised their ability to use a calculator efficiently. At a later stage **Esther's** tutor planned to show her group how to use the percentage key.

Subsequently the tutor explored a variety of applications relevant to each stage of the addition process, gradually introducing a number of assignments relating both to the ALBSU Standards and to the Foundation Stage of Numberpower. As she was trying to avoid the continuous use of paper-based activities, she used a number of board and card games aimed at stimulating students' use of number bonds, by matching answers to problems, for example:

Match the value of the "dominoes"

7 + 8 | 12 | 8 + 9 | 13 | 9 + 3 | 15 | 8 + 5 | 17

Other activities can be based on variations of "Snap", "Bingo" or other familiar games where values are assigned or running totals (such as scores) are kept.

The tutor used **Matthew's** interest in cookery to devise appropriate assignments for him, such as calculating calorie totals of particular meals, or pricing menus.

Esther's tutor wished to ensure that all students in her group could add efficiently, although most were able to handle addition in most normal situations. She introduced a range of assignments which related to Stage 1 of the Standards (see examples on pages 42-44). She also showed students how to handle lists of figures by finding numbers totalling ten:

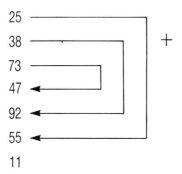

At this stage **Esther's** tutor decided to introduce more complex monetary applications as she felt that most people in the group would soon be ready to work on decimals. She explained the use of the decimal point both in separating pounds from pence, and in separating whole numbers from parts of numbers. The assignments that she used with students made use of both more complex and longer addition problems than those used by **Matthew's** tutor. As she wished to familiarise students with the use of computers in assisting mathematical learning, she initiated students in the use of simple spreadsheets to perform calculations.

Subtraction

Matthew's tutor now encountered a problem commonly faced by numeracy tutors: students in her class already familiar with subtraction had learned several methods of performing the same task. There was also a number who could not subtract at all. In such a case it is crucial to allow students to make use of what skills they do have – to do otherwise can both affect confidence and lead to confusion. It is equally important to standardise the approach that you use with students new to the subject, and to ensure that the method selected is commonly employed in published materials and the school curriculum (as many parents wish to be able to assist their children). You may find however, that you have to try more than one way of explaining something, should the student fail to grasp your original explanation.

GOING ON HOLIDAY

You've got £200 and you are planning to go on holiday to Brighton.

—	Hiring a caravan for one week costs	£80
—	Coach	£15
—	Food	£40
—	Drinks	£25
—	Eating out at a restaurant with a friend	£15 each

Work out the total for your plan.

Check if you allocated suitable amounts of money for each item.

Change your plan if necessary to keep within your budget.

Will there be any money left for unexpected situations?

Make a note of the spending on this holiday.

Record each item and the total.

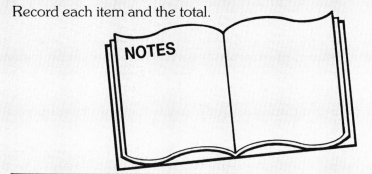

NOTES

HOLIDAY SPENDING RECORDS	£	p
TOTAL		

AT THE POST OFFICE

1. How much is a first class stamp?

2. How much will you pay at the post office to send two letters first class?

3. How much is a second class stamp?

4. Find the cost of sending two second class letters?

5. How many stamps are there in the first class stamp book and how much does it cost to buy one?

6. How many first class stamps can you buy for £1.00?

7. How many stamps are there in the second class stamp book and how much does it cost to buy one?

8. How many second class stamps can be bought for £1.00? How much change will you have?

9. How much will you pay for:

    (a) 4 second class stamps

    (b) 5 first class stamps.

Reproduced by kind permission of Shengul Altan, College of North East London.

Fibre in our food

Skills you need <u>before</u> you begin:

- Reading for information.
- Adding.

Fibre rich foods are good for your health. They fill you up. They stop constipation. They may help prevent bowel problems like cancer of the bowel.

We need 30 grams of fibre every day.

Look at the chart:

- Plan five different menus for yourself from Monday to Friday with enough fibre per day.

These are some fibre-rich foods. The figures show how many grams of fibre each item has.

bread (4 slices)		carrots	3g
wholemeal bread	11g	yam	3g
brown bread	6g	leeks	3g
white bread	3g	dahl	3g
chapati	3g	sprouts	2g
		swede	2g
breakfast cereal (1 serving)		**fruit and snacks**	
2 Weetabix	5g	2 dried apricots	7g
2 Shredded Wheats	5g	1 banana	3g
Puffed Wheat	4g	raisins (30g)	2g
unsugared muesli	4g	unsalted peanuts (30g)	2g
porridge	3g	1 apple	2g
cornflakes	3g	**spaghetti** (1 serving)	
		wholemeal	6g
		ordinary	2g
vegetables and beans (1 serving)		**potatoes** (1 serving)	
red kidney beans	10g	baked in jacket	3g
peas	7g	boiled with skin on	3g
baked beans	6g	boiled without skin	1g
spinach	5g		
sweetcorn	5g	**rice** (1 serving)	
plantain	5g	brown	3g
lentils	4g	white	2g

from 'The Assignment Pack', ALBSU

Matthew could subtract simple numbers on paper, and had devised coping strategies to deal with working out his change in shops based on "counting on":

> To find change from 50p for an item costing 34p
>
> 50 – 34 =
>
> 34 + 6 (making 40) + another 10 (making 50)

Other students explained that they sometimes visualised coins in order to arrive at the right answer, while others waited till they had the change in their hands and worked out whether it was correct by looking at it. Most students stated that they found difficulty in ascertaining whether or not they were given the right change by looking at a receipt. The tutor took the opportunity to distribute a range of receipts obtained from shopping excursions where she had purchased fewer than four items, which were then discussed by the group.

Terms which indicate subtraction

- Minus
- Less
- Decrease by
- Take away/from/off
- Reduce by
- Difference of

Also:

Questions comparing quantities such as:
- How much bigger/smaller/taller/longer?
- How much cheaper/more expensive?

Matthew was already able to subtract single figures, and double figures when no borrowing was involved – the tutor helped other students who were not able to subtract at all by getting them to count back on a ruler or number line. Many students experience difficulty when dealing with "borrowing" and **Matthew** was no exception. Often people have vague memories of being taught the process at school without any clear recollection of how exactly to carry out the procedure. Many adult students will have been taught how to "pay back" numbers they have "borrowed" by adding one to the preceding column on the bottom row:

$$
\begin{array}{r}
\overset{\text{\small 1}}{\cancel{3}}\,4\,- \\
2\,\cancel{1}\,8 \\
\hline
1\,6
\end{array}
$$

Should the student already be familiar with this method, there is no reason to change, but should the student either be completely new to "borrowing", or have forgotten the principles, then it is usual to show students how to use the **decomposition** method:

$$
\begin{array}{r}
\overset{\text{\small 2}}{\cancel{3}}\,\overset{\text{\small 1}}{\cancel{4}}\,- \\
1\,8 \\
\hline
1\,6
\end{array}
$$

The reason for this is that decomposition reinforces a student's understanding of the process of subtraction, and can be explained in terms of place value: when the one is placed before the four in the above example we are really adding ten to four, to become fourteen; when one is subtracted from the three, in the preceding column, we are really taking ten away from thirty, to compensate for the ten we have already "borrowed". This is the method that is currently used in schools.

Matthew grasped this concept easily enough, but encountered difficulty when he started to work with larger numbers:

$$
\begin{array}{r}
{\scriptstyle 16}\ \ {\scriptstyle 1} \\
6\,\cancel{7}\,3\,- \\
5\,9\,4 \\
\hline
1\,7\,9
\end{array}
$$

It is common for students to forget to extend the working all the way. Other common mistakes made with addition and subtraction are shown opposite.

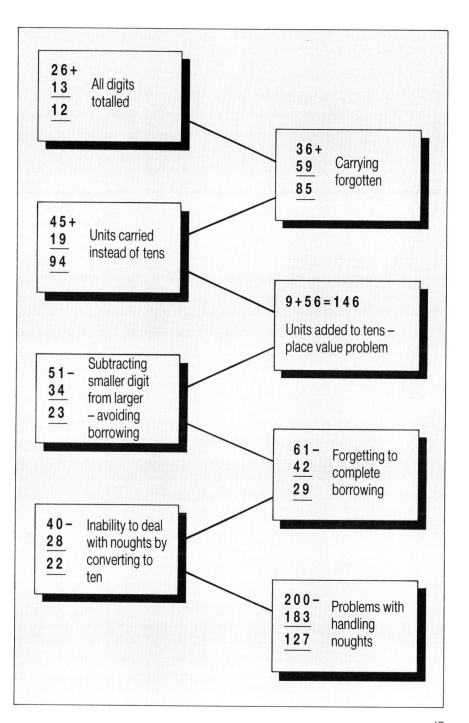

26+ 13 12	All digits totalled
36+ 59 85	Carrying forgotten
45+ 19 94	Units carried instead of tens
9 + 56 = 146	Units added to tens – place value problem
51 – 34 23	Subtracting smaller digit from larger – avoiding borrowing
61 – 42 29	Forgetting to complete borrowing
40 – 28 22	Inability to deal with noughts by converting to ten
200 – 183 127	Problems with handling noughts

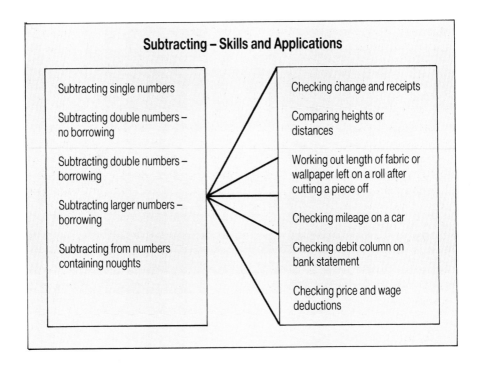

Subtracting – Skills and Applications

Subtracting single numbers

Subtracting double numbers – no borrowing

Subtracting double numbers – borrowing

Subtracting larger numbers – borrowing

Subtracting from numbers containing noughts

Checking change and receipts

Comparing heights or distances

Working out length of fabric or wallpaper left on a roll after cutting a piece off

Checking mileage on a car

Checking debit column on bank statement

Checking price and wage deductions

One problem with teaching students how to use the decomposition method is that they often experience difficulty in dealing with noughts. It is not always easy to understand the logic of borrowing from a nought!

$$\begin{array}{r} {}^{3}\cancel{4}{}^{9}\cancel{0}{}^{1}0\,- \\ 1\ 9\ 9 \\ \hline 2\ 0\ 1 \end{array}$$

In a problem such as the one above it may help to explain the presence of the nine to the tens column as the result of subtracting one from forty (hence also the presence of the three in the hundreds column).

Matthew's tutor was anxious to spend as much time on exploring contexts in which students might use subtraction as on the mechanics of the skill itself. As well as discussing written receipts, she planned activities such as working out balances left in building society or bank accounts after a withdrawal had been made. At this stage she was reluctant to deal with decimalised amounts, because of the difficulty some students had with dealing with whole numbers.

It is also worthwhile using similar games to the ones used to reinforce addition. The tutor additionally used the "Smile" computer game, "Darts", which gets players to keep a running tally of scores in a darts game, which is generated by the computer, by subtracting the latest total (note: students may need to be able to multiply by two or three to work out double or treble scores; this can be avoided by subtracting a score two to three times as necessary). Remember that this game is culturally specific, so further explanation may be required.

Esther's tutor wished to ensure that all students in the group understood and were able to apply subtraction methods, but she concentrated on larger numbers and subtracting from noughts, as most students could subtract smaller amounts adequately. Again she used spreadsheets to illustrate longer calculations and to provide more challenging subject material.

Multiplication

Nearly every student who doesn't know multiplication tables by heart expresses a wish to learn. For some this is possible with practice, while for others it may only be necessary or desirable to learn how to use coping strategies. Should a student not understand the concept of multiplication it is useful to explain it in terms of groups of quantities (*"The Numeracy Pack"*, Diana Coben and Sandy Black, ALBSU contains useful material to support learners with such needs). Many people will add a number three times if they do not know how to multiply, and it is quite useful to get students to carry out a similar exercise to introduce the idea of multiplication, and to stress that it is a less time consuming process than adding the same amount several times.

Matthew's tutor introduced the subject by referring to a restaurant menu and bill for four people which showed the same item ordered more than once on several occasions. She also discussed buying a quantity of the same item in a shop, and working out how much money you would have if you had, for example, seven five pence pieces. She showed students how to use a number square.

Encouraging students to use the square will probably highlight the patterns made by multiplying fives and tens. It is also usually a relatively straight forward process to get students used to multiplying by two and by three. It can be helpful to ask students to fill in number squares with some or all of the squares left blank, or to write down number patterns for particular numbers:

4, 8, 12, 16, 20, ...   7, 14, 21, 28, 35, ...

0	1	2	3	4	5	6	7	8	9	10
1	1	2	3	4	5	6	7	8	9	10
2	2	4	6	8	10	12	14	16	18	20
3	3	6	9	12	15	18	21	24	27	30
4	4	8	12	16	20	24	28	32	36	40
5	5	10	15	20	25	30	35	40	45	50
6	6	12	18	24	30	36	42	48	54	60
7	7	14	21	28	35	42	49	56	63	70
8	8	16	24	32	40	48	56	64	72	80
9	9	18	27	36	45	54	63	72	81	90
10	10	20	30	40	50	60	70	80	90	100

It may be possible to work out multiplication of a given number by 4, 6 and 8 with reference to multiplying by two and 3. For example:

$$6 \times 7 = 2 \times 3 \times 7$$
$$= 2 \times 21$$
$$= 42$$

This method does rely on the ability to multiply double figures (21 in the example above) by two or three, however.

There are two short cuts which may help with the nines table. The first is a paper-based method:

$$6 \times 9 = 6 \times 10 - 6$$
$$= 60 - 6$$
$$= 54$$

$$8 \times 9 = 8 \times 10 - 8$$
$$= 80 - 8$$
$$= 72$$

The second is, almost literally, a rule of thumb:

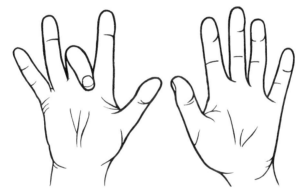

The above example illustrates multiplication of nine by three by showing the third finger held down. The two fingers before the one held down give the tens, while the number after give the units, giving 27. This works for all numbers up to 10.

It may also help students to realise the fact that multiplication is *reversible*. Nine multiplied by five is equivalent to five multiplied by nine. Recognition of this can assist students by reducing the amount of learning that they need to do: if they already know how to multiply by numbers up to eight, then they will already have the knowledge to multiply eight by numbers from two up to seven. Students should be reminded that multiplying anything by nought always equals nought – many forget!

How well students progress with tables will depend on their ability to memorise information – a problem with some students – and on their level of motivation. It is possible to become obsessed with the need to learn them, so it should be pointed out that students will often become more comfortable with multiplication bonds as they become more numerate. Most of the numerical skills that they acquire over a period of time will reinforce their knowledge of multiplication tables, and even should this prove to be difficult there is no shame in depending on multiplication squares or calculators.

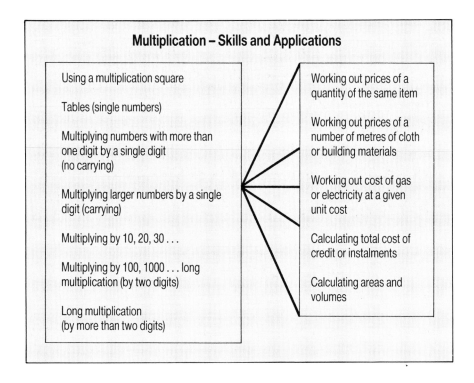

Multiplication – Skills and Applications

Using a multiplication square

Tables (single numbers)

Multiplying numbers with more than one digit by a single digit (no carrying)

Multiplying larger numbers by a single digit (carrying)

Multiplying by 10, 20, 30 . . .

Multiplying by 100, 1000 . . . long multiplication (by two digits)

Long multiplication (by more than two digits)

Working out prices of a quantity of the same item

Working out prices of a number of metres of cloth or building materials

Working out cost of gas or electricity at a given unit cost

Calculating total cost of credit or instalments

Calculating areas and volumes

Matthew's tutor asked the group to calculate the cost of three stamps costing 24p each. She explained that units were multiplied first, followed by tens. **Matthew's** response was:

$$
\begin{array}{r}
2\,4\times \\
3 \\
\hline
6\,2
\end{array}
$$

This demonstrated that he had forgotten to carry to the tens column. When she was confident that **Matthew** and the rest of the group understood the process, the tutor introduced a Numberpower assignment (see page 51).

Terms which indicate multiplication

- Times
- Lots of
- The product of

Also:

Questions such as:

- How much are six pans @ 95p each?

PAYING IN MONEY
AT THE BANK

You are paying in money at the bank on 5 separate occasions.

Fill in the Bank Giro Credit Slips for these accounts:

1. One £10 note and one £20 note

2. One £5 note and one £20 note

3. Two £20 notes

4. Two £20 notes and one £10 note

5. Three £20 notes and one £10 note.

Reproduced by kind permission of Shengul Altan, College of North East London.

Matthew progressed fairly well to multiplication of larger numbers, although he still had to use a multiplication square, and to multiplying by tens and hundreds. The tutor felt that he was now ready to tackle long multiplication, which she illustrated with the following problem:

Assume you want to carpet the living room of your house, and the carpet costs £14 per square metre. If you need 23 square metres, how much do you have to pay?

Before asking students to complete the problem, the tutor explained that when multiplying by the four (of fourteen), the digit represented the number of units, but when multiplying by the one, the digit represents ten, so a nought is added on the right of the second row:

$$
\begin{array}{r}
2\,3\,\times \\
1\,4 \\
\hline
9\,2 \\
2\,3\,\mathbf{0} \\
\hline
3\,2\,2 \\
\hline
\end{array}
$$

The tutor then explained the importance of actually *answering the question:* it is common to respond with a number, rather than a quantity relating to the question – in this case the answer is £322, *not* 322.

There are several pitfalls for the student attempting long multiplication for the first time.

- the order of operations can be confusing
- some students multiply *all* the digits
- nearly everyone forgets the nought(s) at some stage!
- it is easy to forget to carry
- problems set out poorly often are not solved correctly
- it can be confusing to multiply numbers already containing noughts.

Division

The main problem for many students in dealing with division is not so much the operation itself, as recognition of the requirement to use it in the first place. It helps to introduce the subject with a discussion about the range of situations in which students may encounter the need to divide, emphasising the concepts of "sharing", and grouping into equal amounts. **Matthew's** tutor encouraged him to think about times when he shared an amount of money equally among his grandchildren, or had divided quantities in a recipe into equal amounts.

Ways of writing division sums

Twelve divided by four can be written:

$$12 \div 4 \quad \text{or}$$

$$4\overline{)12} \quad \text{or}$$

$$\frac{12}{4}$$

NB. Some people educated in other countries may write division problems in a different way.

Matthew coped with simple division well, but was then set the following problem:

Five friends eating in a cafe received a bill for £35. How much did each pay if the bill was split equally?

Matthew's working was as follows:

$$5\overline{)35} \quad \overset{7\ 0}{}$$

He had placed the seven over the first digit, rather than the second, leading to the error with the additional nought.

When she was confident that he had mastered simple division, the tutor then set **Matthew** this problem:

If you buy a washing machine costing £468 on six months interest free credit, how much do you have to pay each month?

$$\begin{array}{r} 7\ \ 1\ \ \\ 6\overline{)4\ 6\ 8} \end{array}$$

The working above illustrates the difficulty students sometimes have in remembering to carry. **Matthew** was also beginning to struggle with estimating how many times forty-six could be divided by seven, as his knowledge of multiplication squares was yet to become fluent. The tutor suggested that he use the multiplication square to "work backwards", but took care to indicate that he would not locate the exact answer in the square, and would have to find the closest number to forty-six in the sixes row that was smaller than that number. It can be very hard for students to deal with the concept of carrying the remainder forward to the next digit, especially when dealing with larger numbers. It can be equally difficult to deal with remainders *at the end*.

NUMBERPOWER 009.1 (a)

Selecting Goods and Services for Price and Quality

Name .... Date ....

RISE AND SHINE

750g	Sunshine Cornflakes	£1-64
375g	Sunshine Cornflakes	85p
750g	Breakfast Cornflakes	£1-70
375g	Breakfast Cornflakes	86p
375g	Crispy Cornflakes	87p

Which of the above packets of cornflakes is the best value for money?

Remember do not use a calculator to work this out.

© *Anne Tompsett and Julie Fairhead, 1992*
Surrey Adult & Continuing Education Service

Three are three ways of dealing with final remainders:

- leaving the number "left over" as it is, preceded by an "r" to denote "remainder"
- converting the remainder to a fraction
- converting to a decimal.

It is often good practice to introduce the concept of decimals to deal with remainders, as this will obviate any confusion at a later stage – **Esther's** tutor showed her how to use this method and showed her how to divide sums of money where calculation extended beyond the decimal point. **Matthew's** tutor was a little more reluctant however, as she thought that it might be hard for him to grasp, so she demonstrated the first method. Generally speaking, it is not a good idea to introduce the fraction method until you are sure students understand the concept of fractions.

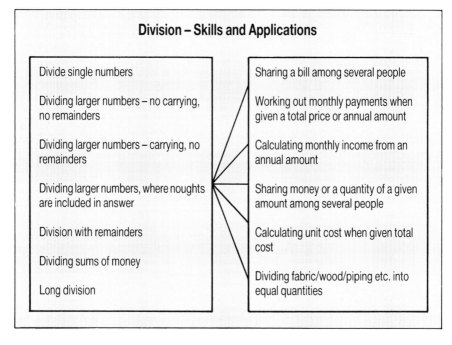

Esther was able to divide simple numbers, but experienced difficulty in dealing with larger numbers, and with long division. The tutor set her this problem:

Fatima buys five plane tickets for her family costing £1535. How much is each ticket?

Esther attempted a solution as follows:

$$5 \overline{)\ 1535} \quad \frac{3\ 7}{}$$

She was puzzled by the existence of the space over the last digit, which had been occasioned by omission of the nought in the middle. This is a common mistake which may be avoided if students are taught to attempt to divide each digit in turn and to insert a nought if they are unable to divide. Students may also find difficulty in dividing numbers containing noughts.

Many people have either forgotten, or have never been able to do long division. Some people remember a little of the process, which can confuse them even more. In real life the easiest way to cope with dividing by numbers larger than ten is to use a calculator, but many students nevertheless wish to master the technique. Unless a student has some memory of being taught, it is often helpful to forget about the formal method that you may have learned at school: students often find the process of "bringing down" digits confusing. It is usually advisable to treat long division in a similar way to ordinary division:

Esther was given the following problem to solve:

The cost of a new car, including interest, is £8976. How much is each instalment, if you have twenty-four months to pay?

$$24 \overline{)\ 8\ \ 9\ \ 7\ \ 6} \quad \begin{array}{ccc} 3 & 7 & 4 \\ & ^{17} & ^{9} \end{array}$$

Esther found it helpful to write down multiples of twenty-four:

$$2 \times 24 = 48$$
$$3 \times 24 = 72$$
$$4 \times 24 = 92 \ldots \ldots$$

Other students may be able to estimate the number of times twenty-four (the divisor) can be divided into eight-nine and so on (they can check their guess by multiplication).

Some people may struggle with subtraction here, and can be encouraged to jot down subtraction "sums".

Esther's tutor discussed the use of fractions to divide, for example:

Find a quarter of £280

She explained that a quarter means "divide by four", and progressed to a variety of examples where use was made of different denominators.

Both **Esther's** and **Matthew's** tutor were anxious to ensure that their students knew exactly when to apply the various operations, and gave them the opportunity to discuss a range of different situations calling for one or more of the four rules of number. They also gave them longer assignments where they had to apply more than one rule to solve a given bill for four people, involving addition, multiplication and division.

As a means of consolidating students' ability to cope with whole numbers, and by way of light relief, **Matthew's** tutor devised a "cross-number" for the students to complete – a kind of numerical crossword, with mathematical problems to solve as clues. **Esther's** tutor on the other hand continued with the practice of using spreadsheets with students.

Rounding off and estimating numbers

There will be several occasions when students will find it necessary to round a number up or down.

- to perform an approximate calculation quickly

- to simplify a large number

- to curtail a long decimal number

- to ensure there are no more than two decimal places in an amount of money.

In practice this is a process with which students often experience difficulty, especially as it entails a sound comprehension of the concept of place value.

Esther's tutor introduced the topic by revising place value, and by ensuring that students understood what it meant to round a number to the nearest ten, hundred or thousand. Particular problems thrown up by students included:

- rounding single numbers down to zero

- rounding a number in the hundreds or thousands to a number of tens

- rounding the answer to a calculation involving money to only two places of decimals.

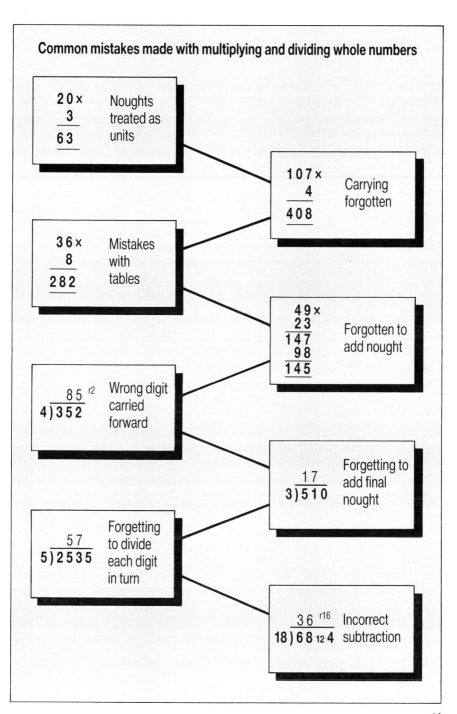

Common mistakes made with multiplying and dividing whole numbers

20 ×
  3
─────
 63

Noughts treated as units

107 ×
   4
─────
 408

Carrying forgotten

36 ×
  8
─────
282

Mistakes with tables

49 ×
23
─────
147
 98
─────
145

Forgotten to add nought

     85 r2
4) 3 5 2

Wrong digit carried forward

    17
3) 5 1 0

Forgetting to add final nought

    57
5) 2 5 3 5

Forgetting to divide each digit in turn

     36 r16
18) 6 8 12 4

Incorrect subtraction

61

Working with time and the twenty-four hour clock

It is surprising that many people do not know how to cope with units of time in an everyday situation, a difficulty which is compounded by the increasing use of the twenty-four hour clock. Some of the contexts which demand such knowledge include:

- interpreting timetables

- setting timing devices such as video recorders

- working out periods of elapsed time.

HEART BEAT

Counting up the pulses.

You are asked to feel a friend's or your own pulse rate.

    a.   Choose suitable <u>time</u> units to work with.

    b.   Set the correct starting time.

    c.   Mark down the pulse rates of 3 people.

....

....

....

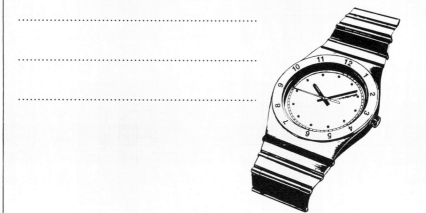

Reproduced by kind permission of Shengul Altan, College of North East London.

Matthew's tutor referred to the ALBSU Standards in planning sessions for her group, particularly the following list of underpinning knowledge and understanding covered by Unit 2.4, "planning and scheduling events":

- units of time: week, days, hours, minutes, a.m., p.m., 24 hour clock and their value

- conversion of units of time: minutes – hours, hours – days, days – weeks

- timing instruments and their uses

- analogue and digital equivalents

- 12 hour and 24 hour clock equivalents

- key words/abbreviations, e.g. minutes – mins, hours – hrs, a.m. and p.m.

- how to read analogue/digital units of time: week, days, hours, minutes, a.m., p.m., 24 hour clock

- how to read diary/calendar formats

- how to write units of time: week, day, hour

- how to round lengths of time up/down

- estimation and approximation of total lengths of time

- how to count on length/s of time to reach a finish time

- how to count back length/s of time to reach a start time.

The tutor set Matthew the following task:

Look at the train timetable for the journey from Tottenham Hale Station to Stansted Airport.

What time train do you need to catch if you want to be at the airport by 12 noon?

How long does the journey take?

If you are meeting a friend arriving on a plane at 12.45pm how long are you going to have to wait until the plane arrives?

If the plane is 35 minutes late, at what time does it arrive?

She had previously discussed the 24 hour clock with the group. Students found most difficulty with working out periods of elapsed time, which the tutor demonstrated by teaching them how to count backwards and forwards from a specific time, for example by counting forward fifteen minutes to 1pm (13.00) in the above example, and then a further twenty minutes to 1.20pm.

Successful completion of the above assignment met the **performance criteria** relating to the unit (by which it is possible to assess whether or not a student has demonstrated competence in the area), namely:

a) units of time appropriate to the context are used

b) appropriate start and finish times are determined

c) the plan is recorded clearly to an accuracy appropriate to the context.

This also corresponds to the Foundation Stage of Numberpower, Unit 2 Element 4.

The tutor then went on to an area relating to Unit 5 of the ALBSU Standards: Setting timing devices and timing activities in everyday situations. She asked students to estimate the time that they took to undertake a number of activities, either at work or at home, and then to time the same procedures accurately. She then asked students to set the video in the classroom for specific times and durations, following instructions that she had simplified and distributed (see also example material on page 64).

Esther's tutor also discussed the 24 hour clock with her class, but at an accelerated pace, as most students grasped the concept quite quickly, indeed some were already familiar with it. She looked at more complex timetables, involving more sophisticated planning and estimation skills. She also looked at addition and subtraction of periods of time.

Using maps and giving directions

A lesson on maps can divert students' attention away from the more number-based mathematical activities, which some may welcome while others fail to see its relevance to what they perceive to count as "maths". **Matthew's** tutor again was guided by the Standards in arriving at a list of skills necessary to give and follow directions:

- units of direction: left, right, north, south, east, west

- units of distance: yards/metres, miles/kilometres

- social sight vocabulary

- essential landmarks

- estimation of distance/s

- estimation of length/s of time

TIMING AND RECORDING ACTIVITIES AND SETTING TIME DEVICES

• Work in pairs, 1 working, 1 recording time.

Situation:

Go to the workshop

Select a piece of timber

50 x 50mm – minimum length 1 metre.

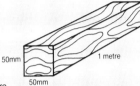

You will also require a **stop watch** to record the time.

Mark off **4 pieces 50mm** in length.

Set the stop watch to zero.

Select a sharp tenon saw and cut each of the 4 pieces in turn.

During each performance time how long it takes to saw each piece.

Fill in the **information** on the following chart.

Timber	Time
Piece 1	
Piece 2	
Piece 3	
Piece 4	
Total	

Core Skills

N:1·2

Basic Skills Standards

N:5·1

N:5·2

205

from 'Upgrade Construction', ALBSU

65

- how to order information
- how to read sketch maps
- how to orient position and direction from a sketch map.

There followed a discussion on the positions of certain landmarks in the borough relative to the college where the class was based. The tutor also asked the students to explain how they reached the class from home in such a way that others could follow the directions they gave. The tutor drew a sketch map of the surrounding area and asked them to locate the places under discussion on the map. She then asked **Matthew** to locate his home on the map, and give an estimate of direction from the college.

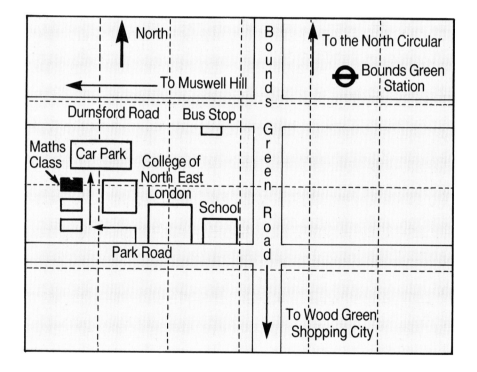

1. Explain how you would reach the maths class from Bounds Green Underground Station.

2. In which direction do you have to walk to reach the class from the station?

3. In which direction is Wood Green Shopping City from the station?

4. If each square represents a distance of 100 yards, very roughly how far is it from the station to the maths class?

5. Explain how to reach the bus stop in Durnsford Road from the maths class.

6. Explain how you reach the maths class from home with reference to the sketch map.

The tutor then introduced **Matthew** to the computer program *"Newtown"*, an adventure game for adults, which practised many of the skills that he had recently acquired, especially following directions and dealing with money in everyday situations (note: this would probably not be suitable for students with more advanced literacy skills than **Matthew's** as it assumes a fairly basic standard of literacy).

Esther's tutor referred her to the London "A-Z", and a world atlas after she had shown her how to use scales and grid references. She undertook an activity in which she was asked to locate a number of places both in London and throughout the world given the grid reference. She was also asked to calculate distances with reference to the appropriate scale.

Dealing with decimals and parts of whole numbers

Students will need to be familiar with decimals in order to cope with money and with metric weights, measures and volumes. Additionally, students such as **Nadia** who are studying a subject with a high mathematical content may need decimals for more advanced calculations.

The concept of decimals, or fractions of base ten, is not necessarily an easy one to grasp, and it can be of considerable benefit if the tutor has included decimals when initially discussing place value.

Mesfin and **Esther** received similar introductions to the basic concepts, using pictorial representations.

Decimals are a way of dividing whole numbers into parts:

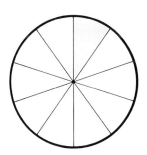

These shapes are divided into ten equal parts.

Each part is **one tenth (1)** of the whole.

We write this as **0.1** in decimal form.

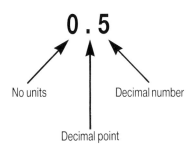

The shaded part of this shape is equal to five tenths (or one half) of the whole.
We write this as:

$$0.5$$

No units

Decimal point

Decimal number

The small square in the corner of this shape is equal to **one hundredth** (1/100) of the whole.

Using decimals we write this as **0.01**.

If you are writing one penny you would write:

£0.01 – One penny is one hundredth of £1 and

£0.05 – Five pence are five hundredths of £1

£0.43 – Forty-three pence are forty-three hundredths of £1

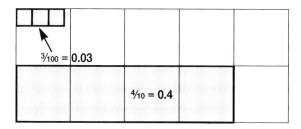

$3/100 = 0.03$

$4/10 = 0.4$

An area of this shape is shaded equal to:

0.4 (four tenths) plus 0.3 (three hundredths)

together, the area shaded is **0.43**

look back at £0.43 (forty-three hundredths of £1)

0.43 is also equal to forty-three hundredths.

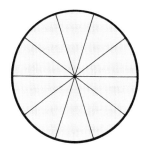
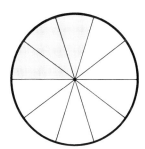

These pictures show one whole shape and three tenths of a shape (shaded areas).

We write this as 1.3.

Write the decimal numbers to go with these shapes:

1.

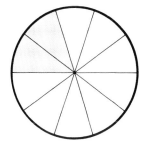

2.

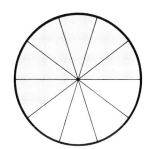

3.

4.

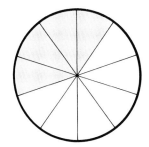 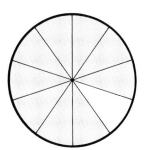

If **one tenth** is written as **0.1** in decimal form and **one hundredth** is written as **0.01**. Can you estimate how to write **one thousandth**?

To reinforce understanding of place value, activities such as the following can be helpful:

Complete the table below:

Number	100	10	1	¹⁄₁₀	¹⁄₁₀₀	¹⁄₁₀₀₀
24.09		2	4	0	9	
60						
1.2						
0.035						
142.3						
3						
0.3						
400.004						

What is the value of the underlined digit in the numbers below (the first one is done for you)?

$$5.5\underline{6}7 \qquad \text{Six hundreds}$$
$$\underline{4}0.2$$
$$3.\underline{1}2$$
$$100.5\underline{0}3$$
$$1\underline{2}.51$$
$$0.00\underline{3}$$

Nadia's tutor ensured that she understood the following:

- the place of noughts in decimal numbers

- arranging decimal numbers in order of size

- addition and subtraction of decimal numbers with the same number of decimal places: (e.g. quantities of money)

- addition and subtraction of decimal numbers with different numbers of decimal places

- addition and subtraction of decimal numbers and whole numbers (e.g., **4 – 1.53**).

She needed to use decimals less in working with money or with metric measurement than in the use of formulae and fairly complex calculations. Some of these could be undertaken by calculator, but neither she nor her tutor was satisfied with being over-dependent on one. To some extent her tutor, a numeracy rather than a mathematics specialist, felt unable to delve into the mathematical content of the course without further consultation with the appropriate subject tutor, and a certain amount of research on her own behalf. The tutor did feel, however, that she could identify certain skills, such as dealing with decimals and fractions, which would underpin the acquisition of numerical skills in the context of the car mechanics course.

    Mesfin and **Esther** also worked on decimals, **Esther's** tutor providing materials related to her interest in clothes making and to general monetary topics, where **Mesfin's** tutor provided subject material relevant to his construction course, for example:

Calculate the total length of skirting board needed in the room sketched opposite (the measurements for the doorways include architraves).

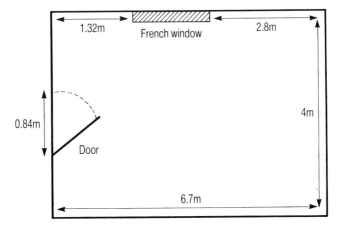

The first calculation **Mesfin** needed to do was to subtract 0.84 from 4 to find the length of the wall with the missing measurements. This was his working:

$$
\begin{array}{r}
4\, - \\
0\,.\,8\,4 \\
\hline
4\,.\,8\,4
\end{array}
$$

Like many students, he did not understand the necessity of adding a decimal point and two zeros to the top figure in order to subtract. It is worthwhile stressing the function of ultimate zeros following decimal points – an allusion to the role of the point and zeros in amounts of money (e.g. £12.00) may help.

Mesfin then proceeded to carry out the rest of the calculation:

$$
\begin{array}{r}
1\,.\,3\,2\,+ \\
2\,.\,8 \\
4 \\
6\,.\,7 \\
3\,.\,1\,6 \\
\hline
14\,.\,4\,8
\end{array}
$$
(the result of 4.00 – 0.84)

He had made a similar mistake in aligning the figures to be totalled. He had correctly aligned the numbers containing decimal points, but had not understood the value of the digit "4".

Other mistakes to watch out for include:

- carrying incorrectly to the left of the decimal point
- misaligning all decimal numbers with varying numbers of decimal places (problems with place value)
- attempting to subtract the larger number from the smaller because it "looks smaller" (i.e. has a smaller number of decimal places)
- confusing pounds with pence if pence are not written in decimal notation.

Multiplying and dividing decimal numbers are more problematic processes, and require careful explanation. All three students worked through a programme broken down into stages:

- multiplying a decimal number by a whole number
- multiplying decimal numbers
- multiplying with noughts to place the decimal point
- long multiplication
- division of decimals by whole numbers
- adding noughts after the decimal point (exact answer)
- adding noughts after the decimal points (approximate answer)
- approximating answers (and significant figures)
- division by a decimal number
- multiplication and division by 10, 100 etc. and their multiples
- long division
- recurring decimals
- decimal and fraction conversion.

Students often make mistakes when counting the total number of decimal places when multiplying – it may help to give a range of problems containing the same digit value but with different numbers of decimal places, for example:

5 x 7	5 x 0.7	0.5 x 0.7
0.5 x 7	5 x 0.07	0.05 x 0.7
0.05 x 7		

Students may also count from *the left*, rather than *the right* when inserting the decimal point in the final answer.

The aspect that is most likely to cause confusion is that of the role of noughts in the answer. Multiplying **0.2** by **0.3** is likely to lead to the answer **0.6**, unless students have a sound grasp of the operation. A more complicated example, **0.25 x 0.12**, gives the answer **0.03**, where students are required both to insert an additional zero immediately after the point, and to omit the "unnecessary" zeros after the digit "3".

Esther's tutor ran group sessions in which she explained the processes to the class in carefully selected stages. **Nadia**, on the other hand, worked through an open learning pack at her own pace, receiving support from the tutor when she needed it. Her tutor encouraged her to use the *SMILE* computer games *"Guessed"* and *"Boxed"* which helps to reinforce decimal place value, and led to further work relating to the size of decimal numbers, and arranging them in ascending or descending order. When a student really grasps this concept, they are likely to possess a far greater understanding of the workings of decimal numbers. Again and again it comes back to the fact that students' success in coping with the decimal number is based on their comprehension of **place value**.

Nadia's tutor in the open learning centre ensured that she understood the principles of decimal division as she worked her way through materials in open learning format. As she already knew how to divide amounts of money by a whole number she was able to cope with the insertion of additional noughts to the right of the decimal point where called for. **Mesfin**, on the other hand, experienced difficulty in solving the following problem:

If you cut a piece of cable 26.7m long into eight equal lengths, how long is each piece?

$$\begin{array}{r} 3.33 \\ 8\overline{)26.7} \end{array}$$

Mesfin clearly forgot to add extra zeros, and merely deposited the remaining digit at the end of his answer. He also found it hard to understand some of the terminology in which the problem was couched (as well as the particular grammatical structure used).

Most students encounter problems when it comes to dividing by decimal numbers – you may find it beneficial to demonstrate to students that, for example, **45.36 ÷ 0.09** will give the same answer as **4536 ÷ 9**, by using a calculator. Rather than emphasising the movement of the decimal point in both cases, it is advisable to explain that you are in effect, multiplying both numbers by a hundred – you can again use a calculator to prove that should you multiply two numbers that you are about to divide into each other by the same number, the result will be the same.

Making Curtains

Hanifah wants to make a pair of curtains for her lounge. She needs 1.26 metres for each curtain. How much does she need for both?

She can only buy material in whole metre lengths. How much does she need to buy altogether?

How much is left?

How wide is each curtain going to be if each piece of material is 1.3m wide, and there is a 0.025 metre hem on each side?

The material costs £18.72 altogether. How much is this per metre?

Hanifah has only got £20 to spend. She needs to buy curtain tape which costs £1.29, scissors which cost £3.35, and two reels of cotton which cost £0.49 each.

Does she have enough money? If not, how much more does she need?

Hanifah finds when she is working with the material that she has made a mistake – she has forgotten about the hem!

She needs 2.5 centimetres, which is 0.025 metres, for the hem.

To find out how long each piece of material must be she needs to multiply 0.025 metres by 2.

She then needs to add her answer to 1.26 metres to find out how much fabric she needs in total.

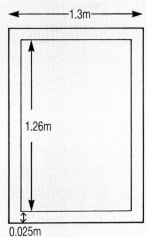

Esther's tutors provided worksheets for her to practise her new skills, relevant to her interest in making clothes (see page 74).

Fractions

It is debatable whether or not all students need to learn how to manipulate fractions. In everyday life we tend to use decimal numbers rather than fractions, which many people find prohibitively difficult. **Matthew's** tutor was content to show him how to work out fractions of quantities. **Esther** and **Nadia** were given a thorough grounding in the use of fractions as attainment of their goals, for **Esther** to progress to an access course, and for **Nadia** to be able to cope with the mathematical content of a course involving algebra.

Mesfin was required to understand the use of fractions in coping with imperial measurement.

Some students may be unfamiliar with the concept of fractions – even grasping the meaning of a half may not be easy. At such times paper folding exercises or using diagramatic representations of fractions may help:

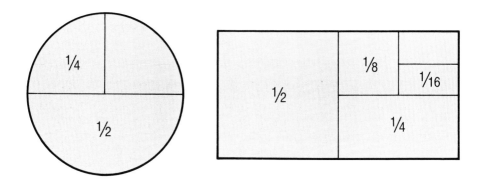

Further practice in exploring the concept of fractions can be attained by working through two *SMILE* computer games: *"Wall"* and *"Tower"*.

It may not be necessary to lead all students through the basic concepts as many will be familiar with them already. A comprehensive coverage of all the key stages in attaining an understanding of fractions would contain the following:

- equivalent fractions

- cancelling and expressing answers in "lowest terms"

- fractions of quantities

- mixed numbers

- introduction to numerators and denominators
- arranging fractions in ascending or descending order
- addition – denominators the same
- addition – denominators different
- subtraction – denominators the same
- subtraction – denominators different
- addition and subtraction of mixed numbers
- multiplication
- division
- multiplication and division of mixed numbers.

In reality, addition and subtraction are more difficult that the other two operations, and may prove a stumbling block for many. It is a good idea to offer a thorough explanation of equivalent fractions (again diagrams may be useful) as this may help students to understand the principles of addition and subtraction. The following example assumes that students know how to find equivalent fractions:

> **A DIY expert is marking a length of pipe. She makes a mark ⅔ inch from the end, then another ¼ inch further along. How far is the second mark from the end?**

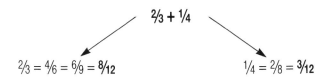

$$\frac{2}{3} + \frac{1}{4}$$

$$\frac{2}{3} = \frac{4}{6} = \frac{6}{9} = \frac{8}{12} \qquad\qquad \frac{1}{4} = \frac{2}{8} = \frac{3}{12}$$

Find equivalents for each fraction by multiplying both numerator and denominator by the same number.

Add ⁸⁄₁₂ and ³⁄₁₂

It may help when you introduce each operation to display an example in pictorial form:

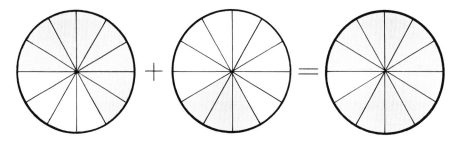

You can do something similar with subtraction, and even multiplication and division, although you will need to keep your example simple.

The other major problem area is likely to be subtraction from mixed numbers where the second fraction is larger than the first, for example:

$$2\tfrac{5}{8} - 1\tfrac{3}{4}$$

The easiest way to deal with this is probably to convert the mixed numbers into improper fractions. In some ways it is better mathematical practice to encourage students to "borrow" a whole number from the "2" by adding eight eights to the first fraction, but most students find that method highly confusing. It is also important that students recognise that three quarters is larger than five eighths, which they will be able to do if they have already practised arranging fractions in ascending or descending order (a quick method is to use a calcuator to divide the numerator by the denominator).

The student will probably progress with multiplication and division more quickly, although difficulties may well include:

- remembering to cancel and to express answers in lowest terms

- remembering to invert the second fraction when dividing

- dividing fractions by whole numbers

- converting improper fractions back into mixed numbers at the end of the calculation.

Mesfin again encountered difficulty with some of the language in which the problems were expressed, in particular the use of the word "of" when multiplying fractions as, for example, in: "three quarters of nine tenths".

Percentages

It is not uncommon for students to react with relative relief when they start working with percentages. Here it is less the actual calculation that is the problem, rather the range of applications that they can be used for.

There are two methods in common use, one of which is based on decimals, the other, fractions. The fraction method is more often used by people educated in other countries and those educated in this country aged about thirty or above. Should a student have clear memories of the fraction method, they should be encouraged to stick with it. The other method is in many ways preferable if students are new to percentages, as it is not dependent on an understanding of fractions. In everyday life it is harder to cope without a knowledge of decimals and percentages, while it is quite possible to manage without anything but a rudimentary knowledge of fractions. A further advantage of the decimal method is that it is easier to work out an approximate answer.

For students such as **Matthew** who are likely to struggle with either decimals or fractions, the use of the percentage key on calculators can be useful, as long as they are taught how to apply their calculations. All students should be taught the idea of **one percent** of **one hundredth** (for example one penny is 1% of pound), and that it can also be expressed as "one out of every hundred". **Matthew's** tutor gave him several activities to complete which involved working out very simple percentages of whole numbers of pounds (e.g. 5% of £1, 5% of £2 and so on) to help him construct a basic understanding of the concept.

It is recommended to discuss percentages in relation to corresponding values of decimals and fractions. Both **Esther** and **Nadia** filled in tables such as this:

Percentage	Decimal	Fraction
1%	0.01	$\frac{1}{100}$
5%		
10%		
20%		
25%		
33⅓%		
50%		
75%		
100%		

It should be stressed that **100%** is **all** of an amount.

NUMBERPOWER

008.1 (d)

Making Payments

Name .... Date ....

A GARDEN BARGAIN

10 metre, 5 Amp,
retractable, complete
£8.99

Sack trolley
£29.45

10% OFF EVERYTHING

Digging fork,
Digging spade
£14.50
each

Shears
£9.65

Work out how much these items come to altogether
with 10% discount in the sale.

© *Anne Tompsett and Julie Fairhead, 1992*
Surrey Adult & Continuing Education Service

Esther and **Nadia** were both by this time familiar with working out fractions of quantities, so they were encouraged to practise using simple fractions with common percentage equivalents as a means of calculating quickly. There are therefore three ways of solving this problem:

The price of a dishwasher has been cut by 25% during a sale. If its original price was £480, how much money is saved?

---

1. $£\cancel{480} \times \cancel{25} = £120$

2. $£480 \times 0.25 = £120$

3. ¼ of £480 = £120

Obviously the latter method is only suitable for a small range of percentage values.
There are a large number of contexts in which percentages are applicable:

Percentages: applications

- price increases and decreases
- wage and benefit increases
- credit and hire purchase rates
- calculation of profit or loss
- calculating VAT
- calculating other direct and indirect taxes
- working out simple and compound interest on loans and savings
- working out commission and bonus rates.

There may be other applications relevant to a specific area, for example **Mesfin** needed to work out timber shrinkage for a variety of different woods using percentages.

VAT (1)

ITEM	@ COST	QUANTITY	COST £	+ VAT @ 17½%	TOTAL COST
Mouldings	90p /m	10 m			
Softwood 150mm x 30mm	£1.50 /m	5 m			
Paint	£15.50 /5l	20l			
Resin wood adhesive	£9.35 /2.5l	7.5l			
Rotary sanding pads	49p /each		11.52		
Fungicide – Weathershield	£2.10 /l		16.80		
Timber stain	£18.20 /5l		36.40		

Reproduced by kind permission of Diana Blofeld, The College of North East London.

VAT (2)

How much would these lists of items cost including VAT?

1. 6m   mouldings

   2.5 litre   adhesive

   1 litre   fungicide

   5 litre   timber stain

2. 15m   150 x 30mm softwood

   12   Rotary sanding pads

3. 15 litre   paint

   10 litre   fungicide

4. 25m   mouldings

   10 litre   timber stain

   5 litre   adhesive

Reproduced by kind permission of Diana Blofeld, The College of North East London.

Many calculations involving percentages are relatively straight forward: calculating taxes, commission and wage and benefit increases, for example. In cases such as these all a student has to do is to work out the appropriate percentage of a given quantity. VAT poses more problems that it used to do, when the rate was 15%, but nevertheless is easily dealt with as long as students understand how to add one half of a percent by the addition of an ultimate "5" to the right of the decimal point (i.e. 17.5% is equivalent to 0.175).

The real difficulties occur when a student is working out exactly what the question is asking. Questions such as:

"Work out how much a woman is paid if she had just received a 5% pay increase, and her annual salary is £12,305".

> **"If a jacket costing £55 is reduced in price by 15%, how much is the new price?"**

entail the realisation that more is being asked for than a simple percentage calculation. With a group it is clearly helpful to discuss how to identify the processes involved. In a one-to-one situation, the student will have to rely on clear oral guidelines from the tutor, or clearly written independent learning materials. It is important however, to make these kind of nuances **explicit**, or many people will fail to recognise them. Profit and loss calculations are more complex, and better left to more advanced students.

VAT (3)

You are preparing a bill for a customer.

Below are the raw materials you used for the job.

Calculate their total cost and the cost of your labour, add on VAT.

12m mouldings

4m 150mm x 30mm softwood

1 litre resin wood adhesive

1 sanding pad

½ litre fungicide

1 litre timber stain

4 hours labour @ £5 / hr

Bill	£
Raw materials	
Labour @ £5 / hour	
VAT @ 17½%	
TOTAL	

Reproduced by kind permission of Diana Blofeld, The College of North East London.

Mesfin found that there was a great deal of terminology that he did not understand, so his tutor took the time to work through with him the kind of vocabulary and phrases that he was likely to encounter both within his own subject, and in coping with percentages in everyday life. He also was taking time to grapple with the way in which mathematical processes are expressed as contextualised problems, as this was not his experience within the culture in which he had been educated.

Metric and imperial measurement

The obvious dichotomy is: which one do you teach, metric or imperial measurement? Unfortunately there is no easy answer, and as both systems are still in common usage in this country students may be disadvantaged if they only have access to one method. Younger people educated in this country may well be versed in the metric system, as well as many of those educated abroad (the latter group are likely to be less familiar with imperial measurement, however). People in their thirties or older who went to school in this country may very well not be able to handle metric measurements. Ideally, students should be conversant with both systems, and able to readily convert between them, but in practice this is not easily achieved.

For anyone ploughing their way through a resource-based learning pack, in an open learning centre, for example, or who is under pressure from the constraints of requiring to improve the level of their mathematical understanding quickly to cope with another course, it is tempting to rely purely on paper-based exercises. No student, however advanced, is likely to be able to grasp the concepts of length, weight and volume in different units unless they have **concrete, practical experience of using them**. This is clearly more easily achieved in a group session where everybody is undertaking similar tasks. Open learning students tend to feel inhibited when they are faced with using measuring equipment in front of a number of students who may be studying a variety of subjects at different levels. There are three possible solutions to this quandary:

- students are encouraged to make use of a practical maths area, possibly screened off from the main learning area

- students are asked to carry out practical tasks at home or in a more private part of the building

- the tutor arranges for students working on measurement to meet together at the same time for a group session.

It should be emphasised that the more practice students undertake in measuring, weighing and using volumes of liquids, the greater their understanding of the processes involved is likely to be. Converting between either units of the same system (e.g. millimetres to centimetres) or between units of the two different systems (e.g. centimetres to inches) is likely to cause confusion unless students have a clear visual image of what it is they are actually doing.

It is of course possible to work with measurement at a number of different levels, even within the same group. The following case studies have been chosen to illustrate this, and could equally well exemplify a range of activities planned for students within the same group, given that the initial practical tasks are shared and discussed by everyone.

Matthew's group engaged in a number of activities related to Unit 3 of the ALBSU Standards, *"Measuring Lengths and Calculating Areas in Everyday Situations"* which required the following knowledge and understanding with respect to measurement:

- units of measure: millimetres, centimetres, metres, inches, feet, yards and their value

- conversion of units of measure: centimetres-metres, inches-feet-yards

- key words/abbreviations, e.g. centimetres-cm, metres-m, yards-yd

- measuring instruments and their uses

- how to interpret numbers/calibrations on rulers/measuring tapes

- how to round lengths up/down

- estimation of lengths

- how to read off lengths using rulers/measuring tapes

- how to add on units of measure to reach a length.

There are two elements relating to measurement in this unit, one of which requires students to measure lengths, the other which requires lengths to be marked up. The tutor distributed rulers and measuring tapes in both metric and imperial units, indicating the relative sizes and positions of the units on the measuring devices. She asked students to measure various objects in the room, such as heights and widths of tables and doors, their own heights, the width of windows, books and pictures. Students were required to use both metric and imperial measuring systems. As a follow-up the tutor asked students to estimate lengths of various objects, and to subsequently check the accuracy of their guesses. During a further class she brought in a length of fabric for students to mark up into lengths. As students were compiling evidence in their Numberpower portfolios **Matthew** wrote a brief report about some shelves that he had measured up from two lengths of timber: a supporting statement was written by his daughter accompanied by a photograph of the shelves.

The third element in the unit concerns calculations of area. As an introduction the tutor explained the concept of area as square units, and used simple diagrams to discuss units of area, such as square centimetres and inches, and their abbreviations. She then asked students to work out areas of specific shapes on a worksheet (they were able to use calculators if they were not adept at multiplication).

MEASURING WEIGHTS

Situation:

A specified amount of nails is required for a job.

You are given a bag of nails taken from a 25 kilogram box of nails.

Weigh them and check that you have been given the required amount which is **3½ kilograms**.

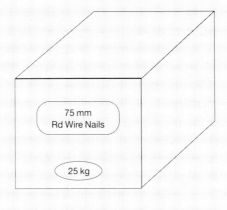

75 mm
Rd Wire Nails

25 kg

Core Skills

N:1·2

Basic Skills Standards

N:4·1

202

Measuring weights and volumes

Element: **Calculating and weighing out required quantities**

You are going to make cakes.

Here is the recipe:

Victoria Sandwich

Recipe A: Imperial
2 eggs
5oz fat
5oz sugar
5oz self raising flour

Recipe B: Metric
2 eggs
150 grams fat
150 grams sugar
150 grams self raising flour

Cream fat and sugar, add eggs and beat.

Add flour – put in cake tins.

Cook 350˚F or 180˚C for 20 minutes.

---

1. How much of each of the ingredients would you need to make two cakes using Recipe B (metric measurements)?

2. When completed, the mixture for Recipe A weighs 20 ounces. You need to divide your mixture into 4 equal parts so you can make 4 buns.

How much would each of the 4 buns weigh?

from 'Basic Skills Assessment Pack', ALBSU

The tutor employed a similar approach with Unit 4 of the Standards: *"Measuring Weights and Volumes in Everyday Situations"*:

- introduction to units of weight and volume
- use of weighing and measuring devices
- practical weighing and measuring of volumes
- estimation of further weights and volumes
- weighing and measuring out of given weights and volumes.

Mesfin and **Esther** also worked on mensuration, but were required to operate at a more advanced level, corresponding to Unit 11 of the Standards. In addition to the underpinning knowledge and understanding required in regard to length and area, they were expected to have or acquire the following knowledge:

- how to convert between millimetres and centimetres
- how to add lengths
- how to estimate amounts of wastage.

Areas of squares and rectangles

The area of a shape is measured by the number of square units it contains. A square unit has sides measuring a unit of length, such as an inch or centimetre.

The sides of this square measure 1 centimetre (cm).

This is called one square centimetre ($1cm^2$) and is the area of the shape.

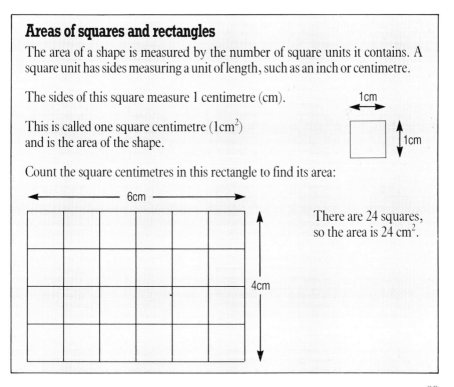

Count the square centimetres in this rectangle to find its area:

There are 24 squares, so the area is 24 cm^2.

Find the area of these shapes by counting squares (the second shape is divided into square inches – in^2):

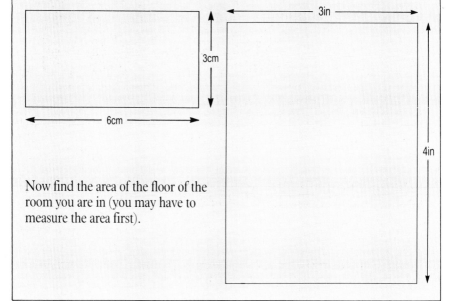

There is a quicker way of finding the area of a square or rectangle:

Multiply the width by the length

Check this is true by multiplying the widths and lengths of the shapes on the previous page.

Find the area of the shapes underneath by using this method:

Now find the area of the floor of the room you are in (you may have to measure the area first).

NUMBERPOWER

Calculating Areas of Rectangles and Triangles

Name .... Date ....

THE BATHROOM FLOOR

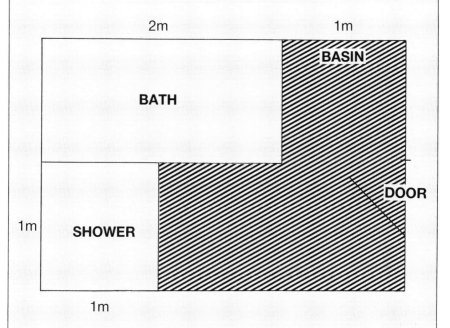

The bathroom floor needs recovering.

Work out the area of the bathroom floor you need to cover in sq.m or m^2. This is the shaded area in the floor plan.

The types of assignment they were given were similar to those undertaken by **Matthew's** group, except that they were of a more complex nature. The practical tasks involved measurement of curved and irregular shapes and of marking up lengths (of material or wood, for example). Their tutors also spent a longer period working on conversion between the various units: students often forget whether they should multiply or divide when converting smaller to larger units or vice versa. They also forget the exact amount by which they should multiply or divide, a facility which only comes with practice. Again it is important to remember that students will be able to visualise the processes involved more clearly if they have had plenty of practical experience.

Mesfin needed a relatively sophisticated grasp of both metric and imperial measurement because of the nature of his course (although metric measurement is more commonly used by the timber trade at the present time). He found this topic fairly straight forward as he was able to use much of the measuring that he carried out on his course as evidence of acquiring the competence.

The remaining elements of Unit 11 concentrate on area, and making scale drawings. In addition to calculation of areas of rectangles, both **Mesfin** and **Esther** worked out areas of composite shapes, for example, of an irregular shaped floor surface, or of a wall with areas of windows and doors subtracted from the whole. Their tutors also introduced the formula for calculating areas of right-angled triangles.

Before either **Mesfin** or **Esther** could be shown how to construct scale drawings their tutors had to ensure that, in addition to knowledge and skills that they had already, they knew:

- scale drawings are accurate representations of full size, two-dimensional shapes

- scales are representations of units expressed as ratios

- key words, e.g. scale, dimensions

- how to express units of measure in decimal notation

- how to divide lengths by 10, 50, 100

- how to multiply lengths by 10, 50, 100

- estimation and approximation of ratios of original lengths.

Mesfin was already familiar with expressing units of measure in decimal form, although he was less confident in dealing with ratios of lengths, a concept which his tutor illustrated with diagrams of pieces of wood and cable of different lengths. He was then asked to make a scale drawing of a piece of furniture that he wanted to construct. **Esther** wished to plan a new kitchen, and research the dimensions and types of furniture and fittings that she was likely to need by visiting a range of showrooms and DIY stores in the area, collecting brochures and price lists.

MAKING SCALE DRAWINGS

1. A client required you to design a new kitchen layout. He has provided a sketch of the kitchen showing shape and dimensions. Your first task is to draw a plan view to a suitable scale.

2. On this sheet is shown the drawing of the kitchen.

3. Reproduce a plan of the inside dimensions of the kitchen to a scale 1:20.

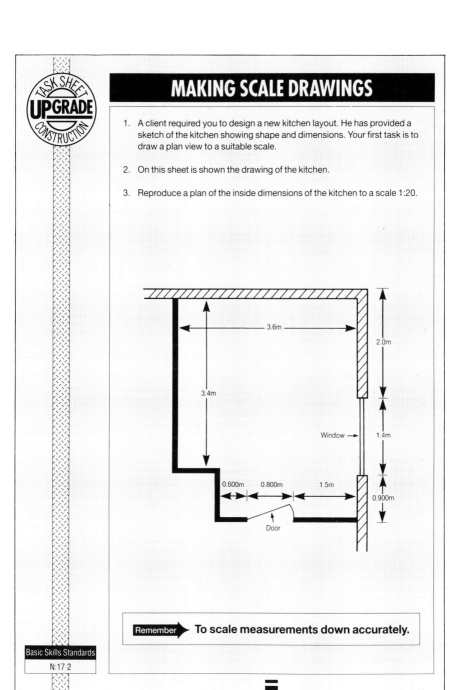

Remember ▶ **To scale measurements down accurately.**

Basic Skills Standards
N:17·2

219

from 'Upgrade Construction', ALBSU

Both students received a similar introduction to weight and volume as **Matthew**, but also learned how to double, quadruple, halve and quarter weights and measures of volume. Recipes provide one of the richest sources of material for these skills, but in **Mesfin's** case reference was made to bulk items used in the timber trade that are either expressed in units of weight or volume.

Nadia covered much of the same ground as the other students, but also needed to learn skills approximating to those outlined in Units 17 and 18 of the ALBSU Standards. She was working in an open learning centre, but had access to a "practical maths" area. The additional areas that she was required to know included:

- formula for area of circles

- key words, e.g. formula, perpendicular height, pi

- how to multiply lengths

- how to divide lengths

- how to substitute lengths in formulae.

The open learning packs that **Nadia** followed included instructions, examples and activities in relation to shapes such as these, given appropriate measurements (she already knew the formula for finding the area of a circle as she had had cause to use it in calculating cubic capacities of car engines).

She also made scale drawings of the ground floor flat where she lives, but in contrast to **Esther** and **Mesfin** selected a scale appropriate to her subject (1:40).

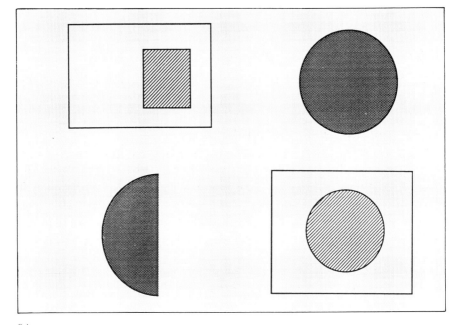

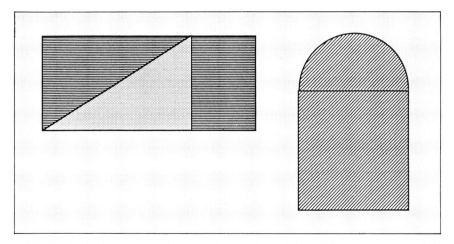

Nadia also had to convert between the metric and imperial systems of length in situations such as buying curtains or carpets, where the required length is measured in yards, but the item is sold by the metre, or working out petrol consumption expressed in litres per kilometre rather than miles per gallon. For this she additionally needed to know:

• lengths can be expressed in imperial and metric units

• imperial and metric equivalents of units of measure

• estimating and approximating conversions

• how to multiply imperial units of measure

• how to read and write approximate conversions of units of measure.

Students might like to use a ready-reckoner, while those familiar with graphs and charts may find conversion graphs useful.

Interpreting numerical and graphical data

Tables, graphs and charts contain much of the numerical information that is used in our society, especially in newspapers and on television. A number of jobs demand the ability to interpret and present data above almost any other numerical skill. As with other topics, study can be undertaken at a number of levels.

Matthew worked on a range of assignments which included:

• using simple tables such as timetables, weather forecast tables and catalogues

• an introduction to pie charts, bar charts, pictograms

• interpreting numerical information such as telephone and payroll numbers and temperature figures.

Getting information from a table

Skills you need <u>before</u> you begin:

- Reading tables of information.
- Working out discounts.
- Multiplying money amounts.

Below is part of a brochure about Discount Coach Cards, issued by **National Express Ltd.**

You can apply for a card if you are aged 16 to 23, or if you are a mature student in full time education. You get about 30% discount off standard fares for a full year. In 1991, the card cost £5.

12 months discount travel for just £5.00!

DISCOUNT COACH CARD
YOUNG PERSON
31 OCT 1992
EMMA MYERT
Colleges

You can get your Discount Coach Card at any National Express or Caledonian Express agent - there are around 2,500 nationwide. Just complete the application form and take along a passport sized photograph (2" x 1.5") for immediate issue. You can buy your first reduced price travel ticket there and then, if you wish! Proof of age may be required, while mature students (over 23) need to provide evidence of full time student status. (At least 15 hours study for at least 20 weeks a year).

National Express and sister company Caledonian Express operate daily scheduled coach services linking hundreds of places nationwide at great value for money fares.

YOU COULD SAVE THE PRICE OF YOUR CARD ON YOUR FIRST TRIP!

Such as	Normal Adult Economy Return*	Saving
London–Bristol	£17.00	**£5.00**
London–Newcastle	£25.00	**£7.50**
Manchester–Bournemouth	£32.50	**£9.50**
Exeter–Cambridge	£32.50	**£9.50**
Cardiff–Leeds	£29.50	**£8.50**
Aberdeen–Birmingham	£47.50	**£14.00**
Oxford–Norwich	£21.00	**£6.25**

*Fares quoted are reserved economy return fares correct as at 10 February, 1991. Standby rates are lower. For full details of fare availability see Agent.

Now, if you are a young person, aged 16 to 23, or a mature student in full time education, you can get about 30% off standard fares for a whole 12 months, for just £5.00! †

What's more this discount is also available on luxury 'Rapide' coaches, and on all Caledonian Express services within Scotland and between Scotland and London. Young Persons only can also get some discounts on certain Eurolines routes to the continent. †
†There are a few exceptions – ask any Agent.

Alternatively, you can apply for your Discount Coach Card by post.

So, either way, don't delay - you really cannot afford to be without your card.

DISCOUNT COACH CARD >>
Incorporating Student Coach Card

1. How much will the fare be from Manchester to Bournemouth if you have got a Discount Coach Card?

2. How much is the Normal Adult Economy Return Fare from Aberdeen to Birmingham?

3. How much would you save by having a Discount Coach Card if you did a trip from London to Bristol once a month for a year?

You can use this for Numberpower Stage 1 Unit 6 Element 1 (A).

from 'The Assignment Pack', ALBSU

His tutor used newspapers and videos of current affairs programmes to illustrate the use of graphs and charts, having initially discussed how symbols are used and how they can represent numerical information.

Both **Mesfin** and **Esther** worked on similar tasks, but the charts and tables contained more variables, and some data was presented as percentages. They also studied line graphs and learned how to report on data both in writing and orally, and how to construct bar charts, line graphs and pictograms. It is clearly important that students have a sound understanding of the concept of scale as representation of units expressed as ratios, and of estimation and approximation of scaled numbers.

They also were presented with numerical data in a range of different contexts, such as catalogue information from which they had to order goods or services, or timetables to plan a journey. **Mesfin** also extracted relevant information from tables listing data pertaining to different timbers. Their tutors also asked them to round numbers up or down, in order to report numerical information. **Esther's** tutor introduced her to the computer activity *"World Count"*, which makes use of a database to display a large amount of numerical data about different countries, including population figures and land areas. As well as providing an interesting introduction to databases, **Esther's** group were able to practise their skills with graphs and charts, calculating averages, and rounding numbers.

Nadia concentrated on similar assignments, although the tables, charts and graphs that she was required both to interpret and to construct again contained a greater number of variables. She also learned how to construct pie charts, for which she had to understand how to use and measure angles, and to insert their value into the appropriate formula. A significant part of the mathematical content of her course entailed interpretation of numerical data, which she brought to the open learning centre to get help from her tutor.

Clearly there are other topics and skills that could be included in a numeracy programme: **Mesfin**, for example, wished to study simple geometry of shapes and angles, whereas **Nadia** needed to progress to study algebra, specifically to help her to understand formulae. Any student either currently, or prospectively studying a subject with a high mathematical content, or who wishes to progress to a GCSE course, will need a grounding in some of the more purely mathematical aspects of number, such as prime and square numbers, factors and square roots.

It is also possible and often desirable to offer students the opportunity to work on assignments which cover more than one or two areas, for example:

- planning a holiday (interpreting information in brochures, the 24 hour clock, timetables, reading a map, budgeting and planning spending, currency conversion)

- planning a DIY project (reading price tables, scale drawing, costing credit arrangements and other expenditure, metric and imperial measurement, areas).

This approach may benefit anyone aiming to gain Numberpower accreditation, as it is possible to compile evidence to contribute to more than one competence through one assignment. It is also often the way that numerical problems present themselves in real life.

Esther's tutor used the chart function of spreadsheets to introduce a computerised dimension to graphs and charts.

The following table contains data concerning the number of students studying different subjects at a college (this is much as it would appear on a spreadsheet):

	English	Maths	Business	Computing
Numbers of students	154.00	144.00	47.00	157.00
Percentage of total	58.33	54.55	17.80	59.47
	Science	Building	Catering	Floristry
Numbers of students	149.00	145.00	63.00	46.00
Percentage of total	56.44	54.92	23.86	17.42

Students can easily manipulate the spreadsheet to present this information as a bar chart:

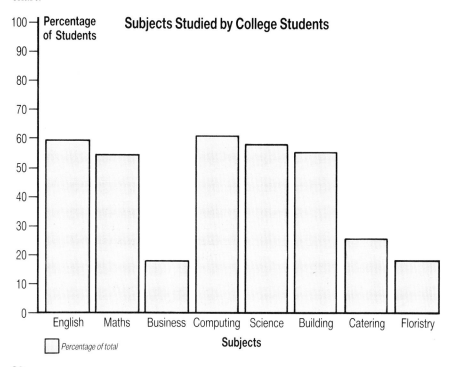

Alternatively, the same information can be inserted into a spreadsheet in a different way to enable a pie chart to be constructed:

	Numbers of students	Percentage of total
English	154.00	58.33
Maths	144.00	54.55
Business	47.00	17.80
Computing	157.00	59.47
Science	149.00	56.44
Building	145.00	54.92
Catering	63.00	23.86
Floristry	46.00	17.42

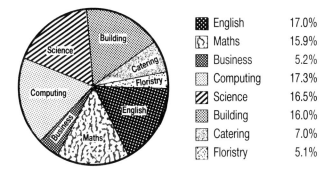

English	17.0%
Maths	15.9%
Business	5.2%
Computing	17.3%
Science	16.5%
Building	16.0%
Catering	7.0%
Floristry	5.1%

Interpreting the chart
Reading a scale

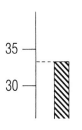

Use a ruler to find the height of the bar on the vertical axis. The height of this bar is closer to 35 than it is to 30 – it's close enough to 35 to be 34 – it's probably 33.

Bar charts do not have a numerical horizontal scale because the items are all separate, and for this reason we leave a space between the bars.

from 'Numeracy for Business', The Open College, page 90

The following pie chart shows in what sort of housing people in a city live:

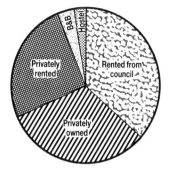

▒	Rented from council	36.6%
▨	Privately owned	32.3%
▦	Privately rented	25.5%
░	Bed and breakfast	3.8%
▨	Hostel	1.7%

(a) Round the percentages off to the nearest whole number.

(b) The number of people in the city is 61,880. Work out the number of people living in each type of accommodation.

(c) Round off each of the figures in (b) to two significant figures.

from 'Numeracy for Business', The Open College, page 95

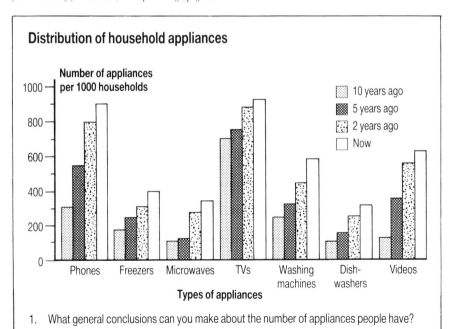

1. What general conclusions can you make about the number of appliances people have?

from 'Numeracy for Business', The Open College, page 96

2. What appliances do people have:

   (a) most of now?

   (b) least of now?

   Note: For the following questions you will have to divide the answers you get from reading the vertical axis by 1,000, as the numbers are for each 1,000 households.

3. Roughly how many telephones per household were there five years ago?

4. Roughly how many washing machines are there per household now?

5. Roughly how many video recorders were there per household 10 years ago?

The following pie chart is more solid-looking than the last one you saw – it looks more like a pie!

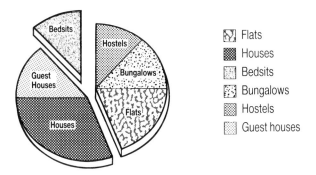

It shows the different kinds of dwellings that people in the borough live in.

(a) Which type of accommodation do most people live in?

(b) What do you notice about the sizes of the other 'slices of pie'?

(c) The population of the city is 61,880.
     Make a rough estimate (guess) about how many people live in each kind of accommodation.

(d) Check your answer by adding the number of people in each group to check it comes to 61,880.

from 'Numeracy for Business', The Open College, page 97

PIE CHARTS

Pie charts show very clearly how an amount is divided up relative to the whole.

Think of the whole circle as 100%. Each section represents a percentage of the whole amount. The bigger the percentage, the bigger the 'slice of pie'.

To find out how big each section should be, we have to have a method of measuring the size of each slice, which is what we call the **angle** at the centre of the pie.

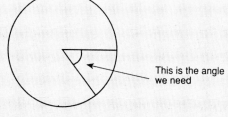

This is the angle
we need

The measure we use for this is **degrees.** A degree measures the amount one line turns or revolves from another. If you had a clock with the two hands on top of each other and you moved the minute hand round completely until it met the hour hand again, it would have **rotated** by **360 degrees** (which can also be written 360°).

You can use a **protractor** to measure degrees:

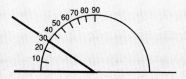

The top line here has turned through 30 degrees.

ACTIVITY

Measure these angles with a protractor:

1.

2.

Answers
1. 20 degrees   2. 75 degrees

(Don't worry if you are 1 or 2 degrees out.)

from 'Numeracy for Business', The Open College

6 | Materials and Resources

This chapter will discuss the kind of considerations to take into account when developing and selecting numeracy materials. It will also look at adapting existing materials, and using other media such as videos and computers.

It can be a daunting task to develop your own materials for the first time. It is so much easier to identify the faults in other people's work than to write good learning material yourself! You also need to consider very carefully both who is going to use your materials, and how they are going to use them. Are you going to use a short extract from a newspaper, for example, as a general stimulus to discussion at the beginning of a lesson? Or are you going to bring in a range of materials at different levels of difficulty to suit different students? Do you want to encourage students to work fairly independently, or together in a small or large group?

Selecting materials

There is an increasing variety of published material that can be used by tutors and students. You may find the following checklist useful to help you select materials:

- Are they appropriate for use by adults?

- Do the students already possess the skills necessary to work through them, or will you have to add supplementary material or oral explanations?

- Is the language suitable?

- Are they relevant to the context in which they will be used, or likely to be of general interest?

- Do they avoid cultural, racist and sexist bias or stereotyping?

- Are they more suitable for groups or work with individuals?

- Are the explanations and examples comprehensible and broken down into sufficient stages?

- Are the materials well laid out and presented?

- Can they be used independently?

**Using money in
everyday situations**

NUMERACY TASK
N5
STAGE 1

Element 1:
Making payments

Your car has failed its MOT and the garage has said you are best advised to buy another.

A. You find a bargain in the local paper for £1200.00.

1. Fill in the cheque below for the cost of the car. The person selling the car is Mrs Elizabeth Stacey.
   Use today's date.

2. You ask Mrs Stacey for a receipt as proof of purchase. Complete the receipt below.

Receipt

Date..

Received from ....

The sum of £...

In payment for ....

....

Signed...

from 'Basic Skills Assessment Pack', ALBSU

Adapting materials

If you cannot find what you want, you may be able to adapt existing materials. You could, for example, add your own examples and illustrations. You could insert additional activities, or either lengthen or shorten a piece. Some materials more suitable for use in a group may be altered for individual use by the addition of clearer instructions, and omissions of group activities. You may also be able to incorporate real life material, such as newspaper or magazine articles, receipts, bills, catalogues, menus or maps, into your own worksheets.

Writing your own materials

It may help to consider some of the key points to take account of when developing your own materials:

- Are you clear about the purpose of the worksheet?

- Materials should be clear and be written in language appropriate to the language level of the student.

- They should be varied and interesting. Visual material can often aid comprehension and increase motivation.

- Materials should be typed (preferably on a good typewriter or computer with a printer of reasonable quality) or written in attractive and readable handwriting.

- They should reflect positive images of women, people from ethnic groups and of people with disabilities (a word of warning, don't go overboard, or you can appear to patronise!).

- They should also avoid being too culturally specific to this country (dealing with money and shops is fine, but not everyone understands batting averages!).

- If you are introducing students to a new skill there should be clear explanations, examples and activities.

- Materials should, where possible, be relevant to students' interests and needs.

- Try to avoid packing too much information onto one page.

When using materials remember to identify:

(1) **what** you want students to learn

(2) **why** you want them to learn it

(3) **how** you want them to learn

(4) how you can **assess** whether or not they have learned it

(5) how you can **evaluate** whether or not they have learned it.

PAYING IN MONEY
AT THE BANK

The Sunshine Playgroup is raising money by running a bring and buy stall every day for a week.

You have agreed to pay the money raised into the playgroup's bank account.

The amount raised each day is shown below.

Fill in the **Bank Giro Credit Slip** – one for each day.

1. Monday   £10 note and £20 note

2. Tuesday   £5 note and £20 note

3. Wednesday   4 x £10 notes

4. Thursday   £50

5. Friday   £20 note and 5 x £10 notes

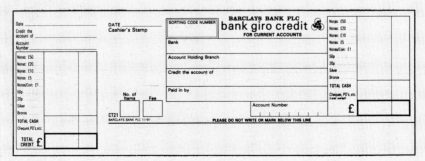

Reproduced by kind permission of Shengul Altan, College of North East London.

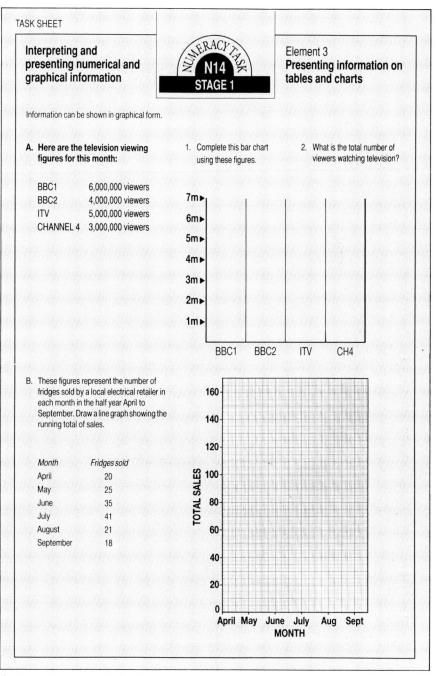

Interpreting and presenting numerical and graphical information

NUMERACY TASK
N14
STAGE 1

Element 3
Presenting information on tables and charts

Information can be shown in graphical form.

A. Here are the television viewing figures for this month:

BBC1	6,000,000 viewers
BBC2	4,000,000 viewers
ITV	5,000,000 viewers
CHANNEL 4	3,000,000 viewers

1. Complete this bar chart using these figures.

2. What is the total number of viewers watching television?

7m ►
6m ►
5m ►
4m ►
3m ►
2m ►
1m ►

BBC1   BBC2   ITV   CH4

B. These figures represent the number of fridges sold by a local electrical retailer in each month in the half year April to September. Draw a line graph showing the running total of sales.

Month	Fridges sold
April	20
May	25
June	35
July	41
August	21
September	18

160
140
120
100
80
60
40
20
0

TOTAL SALES

April May June July Aug Sept
MONTH

from 'Basic Skills Assessment Pack', ALBSU

Materials for use in open learning

In addition to fulfilling the above criteria, open learning materials should have clearly stated objectives, to make it easier for students to assess whether they have learned a particular skill. They should contain self-assessment activities, and the explanations and instructions should be able to stand on their own. It is also very important to include **answers,** so that students can assess their own progress, and learn from their own mistakes.

Computer assisted learning packages

Although some basic skills practitioners have been using computers for some time, it is really their prevalence in open learning centres that has acted as a catalyst for the development of basic skills software.

There are three main types of software in use:

1. Computer Based Learning (CBL) and Computer Based Training (CBT) programs provide instructions, examples, practice and assessment activities, which students can work through at their own pace. All exercises are marked by the computer, and provide immediate feedback. They can be useful aids to independent learners, but may not have more to offer than a good textbook, and can be very expensive.

2. A range of computer games and puzzles. Some of these are more suitable for children than adults, so you have to select with care. There are several excellent programs which help not only to reinforce what students have learned, but also to enable them to conceptualise some basic skills.

3. So called "content-free" software, such as spreadsheets and databases which allow the user to enter their own information and to manipulate it as they wish. These have the advantage of being adaptable for use by students working at different levels, and have a wide range of uses. They can also enable a student to learn valuable IT skills. There are some commercially available packages which make use of spreadsheets or databases to input data which can then be used by the student to perform a variety of calculations or other activities. Some students may even learn how to construct their own calculations, or to program the package to draw graphs or charts. The problem for the tutor in using spreadsheets or databases on their own without access to any of these packages is that they will have to design their own supportive materials, instructions and activities. They may find this well worthwhile however, as the end product should be rewarding and interesting for the student to use, and will only have to be developed once.

Generally speaking, computing activities can serve to motivate and interest students, and help to wean them away from paper-based activities. The better ones can also aid comprehension of numerical concepts, and can be used for both independent learning and group sessions. Specific programs are mentioned in Chapter 7.

108

Using videos

The only commercially produced videos that are currently widely available are the "*A Way With Numbers*" (BBC Education/ALBSU) series, taken from the BBC television series of the same name. These can serve as useful introductions to topics, both for individuals and groups, although you will need to ensure that students watch only that part of the video relating to the area which they are studying, as there is more than one topic on each video. There are also accompanying materials, checklisted against Numberpower.

You can also use videos of television programmes, such as current affairs, DIY or cookery programmes, to illustrate various subjects that you may be introducing to students.

7 | Some Useful Materials and Further Reading

ALBSU has published *Resources: a guide to material in Adult Literacy and Basic Skills (1992)*, which lists the range of literacy and numeracy materials available for work with adults. Each title has been reviewed by tutors working in basic skills.

Basic Numeracy

Basic Skills Series, Henley College.

Introduction to Number (one of series), Henley College.

The Numeracy Pack (Book 1), ALBSU.

General Numeracy

Assignments in Numeracy, Pitman.

BEN Book of Decimals (one of series), BEN Books.

Everyday Maths, Harper Collins.

Facts, Figures and Formulas, Henley College.

It's a Puzzle, BEN Books.

Make it Count: a Fresh Start with Numbers, National Extension College (NEC).

Mathematics: the Basic Skills, Stanley Thornes.

Mathematics: Using the Basic Skills, Stanley Thornes.

Notts Adult Numeracy Pack, Nottingham University.

Real Life Maths Skills, Heinemann Educational Books.

Real Life Problems in Maths, Hodder and Stoughton.

The Numeracy Pack, ALBSU.

Work Units in Arithmetic, Stanley Thornes.

Numeracy in context

Cooking for Fundraising, BEN Books.

Core Skills in Numeracy.

Maths at Work, Harper Collins.

Practical Maths for Woodwork, Avanti Books.

Spotlight on Numeracy, Pitman.

The Whitbread Initiative: Number, Careers & Occupational Information Centre (COIC).

Banking, Henley College.

Introduction to Money, Henley College.

Maths at Work, BEN Books.

Problem Solving – Practical Examples to Promote Skill Transfer, COIC.

Money Matters, Harper Collins.

Survival Pack Series, Jonquil.

Using Mail Order Catalogues, Avanti Books.

Numeracy for Care, Open College.

Numeracy for Business, Open College.

Upgrade Construction, ALBSU.

Upgrade Caring, ALBSU.

Upgrade Catering, ALBSU.

Numeracy in Construction, Harcourt, Brace and Javanovitch.

63, Bute Street, Harcourt, Brace and Javanovitch.

Resources for Numberpower

A Way with Numbers: a Practical Start to Improving Numeracy Skills, BBC Enterprises Ltd.

Crediting Numeracy: Foundation, Stage 1 and Stage 2, ALBSU.

Numberpower Foundation, Surrey Adult Education Service.

Numberpower Stage One, Surrey Adult Education.

The Assignment Pack, ALBSU.

The Modular Delivery of Wordpower and Numberpower, A Materials Pack and User Guide, MAES/Manchester TEC.

Background Information and Ideas and Further Reading

An Introduction to Literacy Teaching, ALBSU.

An Introduction to ESOL Teaching, ALBSU.

Literacy, Numeracy and Adults (Evidence from the National Child Development Survey), ALBSU.

Numeracy Training Pack, Scottish Community Education Council.

Practical Help with Reading, Writing and Number, NEC.

Teaching Numeracy: a Manual for Tutors, NEC.

The Starter Pack, ALBSU.

Using Your Numberpower, Beeline Communications/ALBSU.

Basic Skills Assessment Pack, ALBSU.

Computer Software

Smile – the First 31, Inner London Educational Computing Centre (ILECC).

Smile – the Next 17, (ILECC).

Smile – Eleven More, (ILECC).

Newtown, ALBSU.

World Count, ILECC.

Health Matters, ILECC.

Numerator, Logotron.

You can find a comprehensive selection of software, complete with reviews in *The Basic Skills Software Guide*, ALBSU.

Videos

A Way With Numbers, BBC Education/ALBSU (series of four).

Further Training Opportunities for Tutors

The City and Guilds Initial Certificate in Teaching Basic Skills (Numeracy 9283) is an introduction to teaching numeracy. If you are a practising teacher and interested in gaining a further qualification the following is available:

City and Guilds Certificate in Teaching Basic Skills (9285). This is a competence-based modular scheme, not a taught course. Prior learning and qualifications can be accredited.

Index